Revision Notes
for
Standard Grade
Chemistry

B.A. Duguid

D.R. Glasby

Published by
Chemcord
Inch Keith
East Kilbride
Glasgow

ISBN   1 870570 38 3

© Chemcord, 1993

Seventh reprint 2004

Printed by Bell and Bain Ltd, Glasgow

Note to students

The Course

• This book is designed to cover all of the learning outcomes of the Standard Grade Chemistry syllabus.

The Topics

• The first part of each topic covers all that is required for General Level although in some topics related work at Credit Level is included.

• The second part of each topic covers additional learning outcomes at Credit Level. These are clearly indicated at the start by the Credit code —————— **CREDIT**

• You should check with your teacher whether you should study both parts of each topic.

Your Revision

• Your revision is most likely to be effective if you stop at the end of each page and try to write out the main points.

• You can indicate your knowledge of each statement with a √ in the ❏ at the left hand side.

• Space has been left at the right hand side so that you can make additional notes.

• Additional space is available at the back of the book.

• You can also mark statements with a highlighter pen.

• You are more likely to benefit from your revision if you work at a steady rate and follow a study plan avoiding long periods of study.

• A time-table to help you plan your revision is supplied.

Study planner

Topic	Date	Date	Date	Date	Date	G	C
1							░
2							░
3							
4							
5							░
6							
7							
8							░
9							
10							
11							░
12							
13							
14							
15							
Formulae							░
Equations							
Calculations						░	

G = General
C = Credit

Topic 1   Chemical reactions

CHEMICAL REACTIONS

❑ always produce new substances

❑ can involve a change in appearance,
e.g. colour change, solid formed, gas given off

❑ can involve a detectable energy change,
e.g. heat, light, sound

❑ are taking place all around us in everyday life,
e.g. burning petrol, digesting food, striking a match, grass growing, iron rusting, epoxy glue setting

ELEMENTS

❑ are what everything in the world is made from

❑ cannot be broken down into simpler substances

❑ form compounds when they react together

❑ are arranged in the Periodic Table

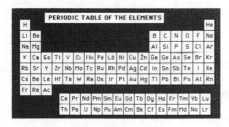

❑ number about one hundred in total

❑ have a name and a symbol

For some elements, the symbol is just the first letter of its name,
e.g. C (Carbon), H (Hydrogen), S (Sulphur).

For some elements, the symbol is from two letters of the name,
e.g. Ca (Calcium), He (Helium), Si (Silicon).

For some elements, the symbol is from the Latin name,
e.g. Na (Sodium from natrium), Ag (Silver from argentum).

COMPOUNDS

❑ are formed when elements react together,

   e.g. salt (sodium chloride), water (hydrogen oxide)

❑ since the elements in a compound are chemically joined, energy is required to break up a compound,

   e.g. silver oxide (heat energy),
   copper chloride in solution (electrical energy)

❑ **-IDE** compounds usually contain only the two named elements

❑ **-ITE** and **-ATE** compounds contain oxygen as well as the two named elements

MIXTURES

❑ are formed when substances come together without reacting,

   e.g. air is a mixture mainly of nitrogen and oxygen

❑ heat or electrical energy is not required to separate the elements in a mixture,

   e.g. iron can be separated from a mixture of iron and sulphur using a magnet, but not from iron sulphide, the compound

Dissolving

❑ a **soluble** substance dissolves in a liquid

❑ an **insoluble** substance does not dissolve in a liquid

❑ the **solvent** is the liquid in which the substance dissolves

❑ \the **solute** is the substance which dissolves in a liquid

❑ a solute can be a solid, a liquid or a gas,

   e.g. sugar (solid), alcohol (liquid), sulphur dioxide (gas)

❑ a **solution** is formed when a solute dissolves in a solvent

❑ in an **aqueous** solution water is the solvent,

   e.g. in an aqueous sugar solution, sugar is the solute and water is the solvent

Topic 2   Speed of reactions

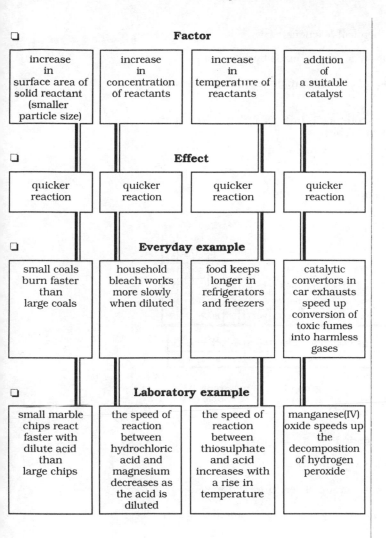

❏   **Factor**

| increase in surface area of solid reactant (smaller particle size) | increase in concentration of reactants | increase in temperature of reactants | addition of a suitable catalyst |

❏   **Effect**

| quicker reaction | quicker reaction | quicker reaction | quicker reaction |

❏   **Everyday example**

| small coals burn faster than large coals | household bleach works more slowly when diluted | food keeps longer in refrigerators and freezers | catalytic convertors in car exhausts speed up conversion of toxic fumes into harmless gases |

❏   **Laboratory example**

| small marble chips react faster with dilute acid than large chips | the speed of reaction between hydrochloric acid and magnesium decreases as the acid is diluted | the speed of reaction between thiosulphate and acid increases with a rise in temperature | manganese(IV) oxide speeds up the decomposition of hydrogen peroxide |

CATALYSTS

❏   speed up some reactions

❏   are not used up during reactions

❏   can be recovered chemically unchanged

Topic 3   Atoms and the Periodic Table

ELEMENTS   (see Chemical reactions)

❑   can be naturally occurring or made by scientists

❑   can be solid, liquid or gas (bromine and mercury are the two liquids)

❑   can be metals or non-metals (metals are on the left-hand side of the Periodic Table)

PERIODIC TABLE

❑   a chart which lists all the elements

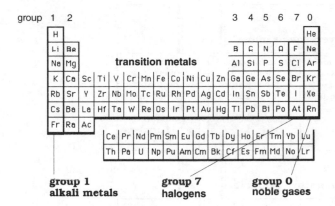

group 1 2   3 4 5 6 7 0

group 1
alkali metals

group 7
halogens

group 0
noble gases

❑   a row is called a **period**

❑   a column is called a **group**

❑   the **noble gases** is a group of very unreactive elements

❑   the **alkali metals** are very reactive and stored under oil

ATOMS

❑   are the very small particles which make up every element

❑   each element contains only one kind of atom (but see isotopes)

❑   the small core at the centre of the atom is called the **nucleus**

- the nucleus is positively charged

- **electrons** move through space outside the nucleus

- electrons are arranged in **energy levels (shells)**

- the first energy level can hold up to 2 electrons;
  the second energy level can hold up to 8 electrons;
  the third energy level can hold up to 8 electrons

- the electron arrangements of atoms of elements are given
  on page 1 of the Data Booklet

- electrons are negatively charged

- an atom is neutral because the negative charge of the
  electrons is equal to the positive charge of the nucleus
  (but see ions)

- atoms of different elements vary in size and mass

- atoms of different elements have a different number in the
  Periodic Table called the **atomic number**

KEY		
Atomic number	1	
Symbol	**H**	
Electron arrangement	1	
Name	Hydrogen	

Group 1	Group 2	Group 3	Group 4	Group 5	Group 6	Group 7	Group 0
							2 **He** 2 Helium
3 **Li** 2,1 Lithium	4 **Be** 2,2 Beryllium	5 **B** 2,3 Boron	6 **C** 2,4 Carbon	7 **N** 2,5 Nitrogen	8 **O** 2,6 Oxygen	9 **F** 2,7 Fluorine	10 **Ne** 2,8 Neon
11 **Na** 2,8,1 Sodium	12 **Mg** 2,8,2 Magnesium	13 **Al** 2,8,3 Aluminium	14 **Si** 2,8,4 Silicon	15 **P** 2,8,5 Phosphorus	16 **S** 2,8,6 Sulphur	17 **Cl** 2,8,7 Chlorine	18 **Ar** 2,8,8 Argon
19 **K** 2,8,8,1 Potassium	20 **Ca** 2,8,8,2 Calcium						

- elements are arranged in order of increasing atomic
  number

- elements in the same group have the same number of
  outer electrons and have similar chemical properties

Inside the atom

❏ atoms are made up of smaller particles

	Charge	Mass	Position in the atom
PROTON	+ve 1	1 amu	nucleus
ELECTRON	-ve 1	neglible	energy level (shell)
NEUTRON	zero	1 amu	nucleus

❏ an atom is neutral because the number of protons is equal to the number of electrons (but see ions)

❏ the number of protons in the nucleus is equal to the **atomic number**

❏ the atomic number gives the number of electrons in an atom (but not an ion)

❏ the **mass number** is the total number of protons plus neutrons in the nucleus

❏ the atomic number and mass number allow the number of protons, neutrons and electrons in an atom to be determined

Atomic number —— see Periodic Table

Mass number —— not in Periodic Table has to be given

Number of protons — equal to atomic number

Number of neutrons — mass number minus number of protons

Number of electrons — equal to number of protons

❑   **isotopes** are atoms of the one element with different mass numbers

❑   isotopes have the same atomic number (number of protons) but different numbers of neutrons

❑   the **relative atomic mass** is the average mass of an atom of an element allowing for the different isotopes present and their percentage proportions

❑   since it is an average, the relative atomic mass is usually not a whole number,

    e.g. the relative atomic mass of chlorine is 35.5

❑   since it is relative to the mass of other atoms, there are no units

❑   the relative atomic masses of some elements are given on page 4 of the Data Booklet

❑   the Data Booklet simplifies most values to the nearest whole number

Symbols

❑   the atomic number and mass number are often written with the chemical symbols as shown:

$$\begin{matrix} \text{mass number} & 37 \\ \text{atomic number} & 17 \end{matrix} \text{Cl}$$

17 protons   (atomic number)
20 neutrons   (mass number minus atomic number)
17 electrons   (number of protons equals number of electrons)

Topic 4   How atoms combine

COVALENT BONDING

❏ atoms can be held together by **bonds**

❏ involves atoms sharing a pair of electrons

❏ in forming a covalent bond atoms achieve the same electron arrangement as an atom of a noble gas; this electron arrangement is stable

❏ usually only atoms of non-metal elements form covalent bonds

❏ a **molecule** is a group of atoms held together by covalent bonds

❏ a **diatomic** molecule contains two atoms joined together,
  e.g. hydrogen (H_2), hydrogen chloride (HCl)

❏ the **chemical formula** of a covalent substance gives the number of atoms of each element in a molecule of the substance,
  e.g. hydrogen oxide (H_2O), nitrogen hydride (NH_3)

❏ the elements which are made up of diatomic molecules are:

hydrogen	H_2	nitrogen	N_2
oxygen	O_2	fluorine	F_2
chlorine	Cl_2	bromine	Br_2
iodine	I_2		

❏ an oxygen molecule has a double covalent bond;
  a nitrogen molecule has a triple covalent bond;
  the diatomic molecules of other elements consist of single covalent bonds

❏ the **full structural formula** shows the way in which the atoms in a molecule are arranged,

  e.g. hydrogen oxide

$$\begin{array}{ccc} & O & \\ & \diagup\;\diagdown & \\ H & & H \end{array}$$

  carbon chloride

$$\begin{array}{c} Cl \\ | \\ Cl - C - Cl \\ | \\ Cl \end{array}$$

ELECTRON CLOUDS

❏ the electrons in the energy levels are arranged in electron clouds

❏ an electron cloud is a volume of space with a definite shape

❏ each electron cloud can hold a maximum of two electrons

❏ one cloud, shaped like a sphere, makes up the first energy level

❏ four clouds, which point towards the corners of a tetrahedron, make up the second and third energy levels

❏ the clouds which make up the third energy level are bigger and extend further away from the nucleus

❏ where possible, each cloud is occupied by a single electron; this decides the way in which electron clouds are filled,

   e.g. the outer electron clouds of hydrogen and sulphur can be represented:

   hydrogen   *sulphur*

electron clouds have been
"flattened"

❏ the merging of half-filled outer electron clouds can be shown by electron sharing diagrams,

   e.g. hydrogen sulphide H_2S

❑ the shapes of molecules are based on the tetrahedral arrangement of electrons,

  e.g. hydrogen oxide H_2O

  nitrogen hydride NH_3

  carbon tetrachloride CCl_4

COVALENT BOND

❑ the protons give a positive charge to the nucleus of the atom

❑ the electrons give a negative charge to the part of the atom surrounding the nucleus

❑ in a covalent bond the merging of half-filled clouds increases the negative charge in the overlap region

❑ the positive nuclei of both atoms attract the electrons in the overlap region and this holds the atoms together,

  e.g. hydrogen

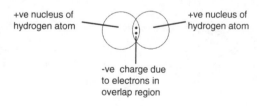

+ve nucleus of hydrogen atom

+ve nucleus of hydrogen atom

-ve charge due to electrons in overlap region

+ve   <------------>   -ve   <------------>   +ve
      attraction   attraction

❑ a lot of energy is required to overcome the forces of attraction and break covalent bonds

Topic 5   Fuels

Changes of state

❏ substances have specific melting and boiling points

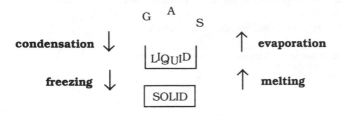

G A S

condensation ↓   ↑ evaporation

LIQUID

freezing ↓   ↑ melting

SOLID

FUELS

❏ are chemicals which burn (react with oxygen) releasing energy

❏ **combustion** is another word for burning

❏ an **exothermic reaction** is one in which energy is released

❏ **fossil fuels** are formed from animal or plant remains,
   e.g. coal, oil, natural gas

	Coal	**Oil**	**Natural gas**
How formed	decay of vegetation in swamps	decay of marine organisms	with both coal and oil
What it is	80 - 99% carbon; nitrogen, sulphur and carbon compounds	carbon and sulphur compounds	mainly methane
Principle uses	source of electrical power; also coke for extraction of metals from ores	source of gaseous and liquid fuels	domestic and industrial fuel

❏ fossil fuels are **finite resources**, i.e. cannot be replaced

❏ over-use of fossil fuels may lead to a **fuel crisis**

❏ the carbon compounds which are found in oil and natural gas are mainly hydrocarbons

❏ **hydrocarbons** are compounds of hydrogen and carbon only

FRACTIONAL DISTILLATION

❑ **crude oil** is the mixture of hydrocarbons as it comes from the ground or sea-bed

❑ is the process used to separate the different hydrocarbons in crude oil according to their boiling points

❑ a group of hydrocarbons with boiling points within a given range is called a **fraction**,

   e.g. petroleum gas, gasoline, kerosine, gas oils, residue

	Petroleum gas	Gasoline (naphtha)	Kerosine	Gas oils	Residue
Number of carbon atoms	1 - 4	5 - 10	11 - 12	13 - 25	25+
Ease of evaporation	← easier to evaporate				
Viscosity	becoming thicker →				
Flammability	← easier to ignite				
Boiling point range / °C	-160 to 20	20 to 120	120 to 240	240 to 350	over 350
Examples of use	calor gas fuel	petrol fuel	jet aircraft fuel, paraffin for lamps	diesel fuel	lubricants, waxes, road tar

❑ as molecular size increases the boiling point increases (harder to move heavy molecules fast enough for escape from liquid)

❑ as molecular size increases flammability decreases (less likely to be a vapour)

❑ as molecular size increases viscosity increases (longer molecules become tangled up)

To do with fuels

❑	Where found /formed	Combustion	Test
nitrogen	approx 80% of the air	does not burn	
oxygen	approx 20% of the air	reacts when a substance burns	relights a glowing splint
argon and other noble gases	approx 1% of the air	do not burn	
carbon dioxide	0.04% of the air; formed in the complete combustion of fossil fuels	does not burn	turns calcium hydroxide solution (lime water) cloudy
carbon monoxide	formed in the incomplete combustion of fossil fuels	burns to form carbon dioxide only	
carbon	formed in the incomplete combustion of fossil fuels	complete combustion gives carbon dioxide; incomplete combustion gives carbon monoxide	
water	formed in the burning of fossil fuels	does not burn	melts at 0 °C; boils at 100 °C
sulphur dioxide	formed in the burning of fossil fuels	does not burn	acidic gas; choking effect
methane and other hydrocarbon gases and liquids	natural gas and oil; formed from coal	complete combustion gives carbon dioxide and water	
lead compounds	added to petrol; given out in car exhaust fumes	do not burn	

POLLUTION

❑ in car engines, the electrical spark provides the energy which results in nitrogen reacting with the oxygen of the air to form oxides of nitrogen; these poisonous gases contribute to the acid rain problem

❑ sulphur compounds in fossil fuels burn to produce sulphur dioxide which contributes to the acid rain problem; removing sulphur compounds reduces air pollution

- carbon monoxide is a poisonous gas which combines with haemoglobin in the blood

- air pollution from the burning of hydrocarbons can be reduced by special exhaust systems in which transition metal catalysts convert pollutant gases to harmless gases (catalytic converters); decreasing the fuel to the air ratio improves the efficiency of combustion thus decreasing pollution

- carbon dioxide has been building up in the atmosphere due to increased burning of fossil fuels (greenhouse effect); use less fossil fuels to reduce this problem

- lead compounds in the atmosphere contribute to pollution problems; the use of lead-free petrol reduces this problem

Burning fuels

- fuels can be burned in the laboratory

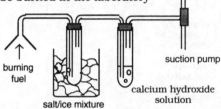

burning fuel

salt/ice mixture

suction pump

calcium hydroxide solution

- if the calcium hydroxide solution turns milky, carbon dioxide must be produced; the fuel must contain carbon

- if a colourless liquid collects in the tube surrounded by the salt/ice mixture the boiling point and freezing point can be taken; if the liquid boils at 100 $^\circ$C and freezes at 0 $^\circ$C water must be produced; the fuel must contain hydrogen

Topic 6

<h1 style="text-align:center">Structures and reactions of hydrocarbons</h1>

ALKANES

❑ are a subset of the set of hydrocarbons

❑ contain only carbon to carbon bonds which are single covalent

❑ the names of the alkanes have a prefix which indicates the number of carbon atoms in the molecule and end in **-ane**

Number of carbons	Prefix
1	meth-
2	eth-
3	prop-
4	but-
5	pent-
6	hex-
7	hept-
8	oct-

❑ **saturated** hydrocarbons contain only carbon to carbon single covalent bonds,

e.g. the alkanes

❑ **Source**   natural gas:
fractional distillation of crude oil

❑ **Physical properties** CH_4 to C_4H_{10} are gases;
C_5H_{12} to $C_{17}H_{36}$ are liquids;
$C_{18}H_{38}$ upwards are solids;
all are insoluble in water

❑ **Uses**   as gaseous fuels (e.g. methane in gas cookers);
as liquid fuels (e.g. petrol for cars);
lubricants; bitumen

❑ burn in a plentiful supply of air to produce carbon dioxide and water; in a limited supply of air carbon monoxide (and carbon) may be produced

1
methane

H
|
H–C–H
|
H

CH_4
CH_4

2
ethane

H H
| |
H–C–C–H
| |
H H

CH_3-CH_3
C_2H_6

3
propane

H H H
| | |
H–C–C–C–H
| | |
H H H

CH_3-CH_2-CH_3
C_3H_8

4
butane

H H H H
| | | |
H–C–C–C–C–H
| | | |
H H H H

CH_3-CH_2-CH_2-CH_3
C_4H_{10}

5
pentane

H H H H H
| | | | |
H–C–C–C–C–C–H
| | | | |
H H H H H

CH_3-CH_2-CH_2-CH_2-CH_3
C_5H_{12}

6
hexane

H H H H H H
| | | | | |
H–C–C–C–C–C–C–H
| | | | | |
H H H H H H

CH_3-CH_2-CH_2-CH_2-CH_2-CH_3
C_6H_{14}

7
heptane

H H H H H H H
| | | | | | |
H–C–C–C–C–C–C–C–H
| | | | | | |
H H H H H H H

CH_3-CH_2-CH_2-CH_2-CH_2-CH_2-CH_3
C_7H_{16}

8
octane

H H H H H H H H
| | | | | | | |
H–C–C–C–C–C–C–C–C–H
| | | | | | | |
H H H H H H H H

CH_3-CH_2-CH_2-CH_2-CH_2-CH_2-CH_2-CH_3
C_8H_{18}

❏   the general formula for alkanes is C_nH_{2n+2}

ALKENES

❑ are another subset of the set of hydrocarbons

❑ contain at least one carbon to carbon double covalent bond

❑ all names have a prefix which indicates the number of carbon atoms in the molecule and end in **-ene**

❑ **unsaturated** hydrocarbons contain at least one carbon to carbon double covalent bond,
 e.g. the alkenes

❑ burn in a plentiful supply of air to produce carbon dioxide and water

❑ undergo **addition** reactions with bromine
 e.g.

$$\underset{H}{\overset{H}{\diagdown}}C=\underset{H}{\overset{H}{\underset{|}{\overset{|}{C}}}}-\underset{H}{\overset{H}{\underset{|}{\overset{|}{C}}}}-H \ + \ Br_2 \ \rightarrow \ H-\underset{Br}{\overset{H}{\underset{|}{\overset{|}{C}}}}-\underset{Br}{\overset{H}{\underset{|}{\overset{|}{C}}}}-\underset{H}{\overset{H}{\underset{|}{\overset{|}{C}}}}-H$$

❑ in this reaction the bromine atoms add on at either side of the carbon to carbon double bond

❑ this reaction can be used as the test to distinguish unsaturated hydrocarbons from saturated hydrocarbons

❑ undergo **addition** reactions with hydrogen,

 e.g. propene + hydrogen → propane

❑ are used to make plastics,
 e.g. polythene, polystyrene, PVC

2
ethene
$\underset{H}{\overset{H}{\diagdown}}C=C\underset{H}{\overset{H}{\diagup}}$
$CH_2=CH_2$
C_2H_4

KEY
Number of carbon atoms
Name
Full structural formula
Shortened structural formula
Molecular formula

3	4
propene	butene
$H-\overset{H}{\underset{H}{C}}-\overset{H}{C}=C\underset{H}{\overset{H}{\diagup}}$	$H-\overset{H}{\underset{H}{C}}-\overset{H}{\underset{H}{C}}-\overset{H}{C}=C\underset{H}{\overset{H}{\diagup}}$
$CH_3\text{-}CH=CH_2$	$CH_3\text{-}CH_2\text{-}CH=CH_2$
C_3H_6	C_4H_8

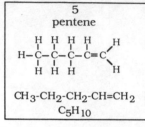

5
pentene

$CH_3\text{-}CH_2\text{-}CH_2\text{-}CH\text{=}CH_2$
C_5H_{10}

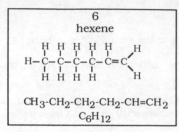

6
hexene

$CH_3\text{-}CH_2\text{-}CH_2\text{-}CH_2\text{-}CH\text{=}CH_2$
C_6H_{12}

❑ the general formula for the alkenes is C_nH_{2n}

Oil industry

❑ crude oil is a mixture of hydrocarbons; this mixture is separated into fractions by fractional distillation (see Fuels)

❑ there is a surplus of the fractions containing molecules of high molecular mass

❑ **catalytic cracking** is a process which breaks unwanted large molecules into smaller more useful molecules,
   e.g. petrol and diesel

❑ alkenes are also produced,
   e.g. ethene, propene, butene

❑ catalytic cracking can be carried out in the laboratory using an aluminium oxide catalyst

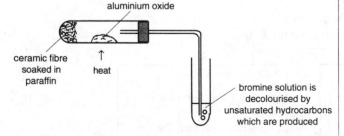

aluminium oxide

ceramic fibre
soaked in
paraffin

↑
heat

bromine solution is
decolourised by
unsaturated hydrocarbons
which are produced

❑ the mixture of saturated and unsaturated hydrocarbons is a result of the breaking of different carbon to carbon bonds in different molecules,

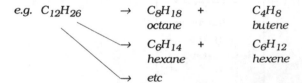

e.g. $C_{12}H_{26}$ → C_8H_{18} + C_4H_8
   octane   *butene*

   → C_6H_{14} + C_6H_{12}
   hexane   *hexene*

   → *etc*

❑ the catalyst speeds up the reaction allowing it to take place at a lower temperature

CYCLOALKANES

❏ are another subset of the set of hydrocabons

❏ all have a "ring" of carbon atoms and contain only carbon to carbon bonds which are single covalent

❏ all have cyclo- in the name followed by a prefix which indicates the number of carbon atoms in the molecule and the -**ane** ending

---

3
cyclopropane

$$CH_2$$
$$CH_2\text{-}CH_2$$

$$C_3H_6$$

KEY

Number of carbon atoms
Name
Full structural formula
Shortened structural formula
Molecular formula

4
cyclobutane

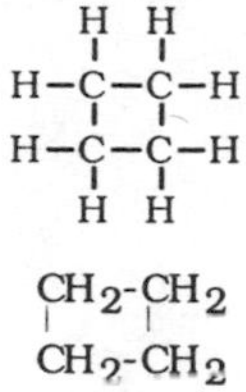

$$CH_2\text{-}CH_2$$
$$CH_2\text{-}CH_2$$

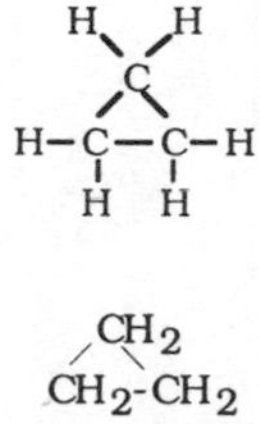

$$C_4H_8$$

5
cyclopentane

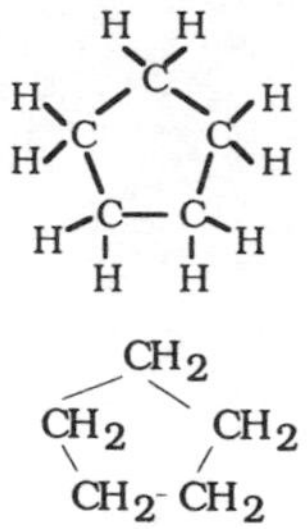

$$CH_2$$
$$CH_2 \quad CH_2$$
$$CH_2\text{-}CH_2$$

$$C_5H_{10}$$

6
cyclohexane

$$CH_2\text{-}CH_2$$
$$CH_2 \quad CH_2$$
$$CH_2\text{-}CH_2$$

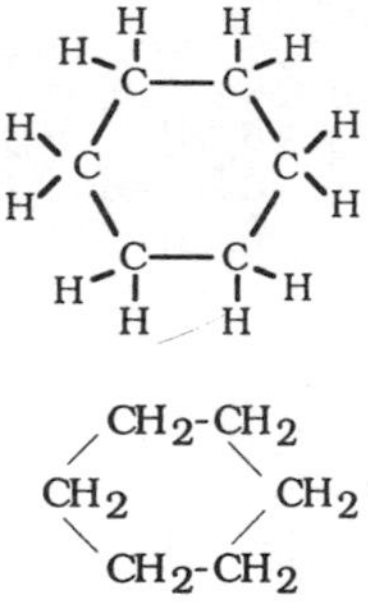

$$C_6H_{12}$$

❏ the general formula for the cycloalkanes is C_nH_{2n}

❏ the cycloalkanes can be distinguished from alkenes using bromine solution; alkenes decolourise the solution

HOMOLOGOUS SERIES

❑ a set of compounds with the same general formula and similar chemical properties,

e.g. alkanes, (C_nH_{2n+2}), alkenes, (C_nH_{2n}), cycloalkanes (C_nH_{2n})

ISOMERS

❑ are compounds with the same molecular formula but different structural formulae

❑ the following diagram may be useful in deciding whether or not pairs of compounds are isomers

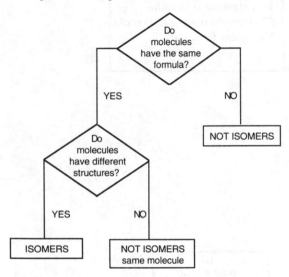

Examples

H H H
H–C–C–C–H
H H H

H H H H
H–C–C–C–C–H
H H H H

not isomers

H H H H
H–C–C–C–C–H
H H H H

H
H–C–H
H H
H–C–C–C–H
H H H

isomers

H H
H–C–C–H
H
H–C–C–H
H H

H H H H
H–C–C–C–C–H
H H H H

not isomers

isomers

not isomers

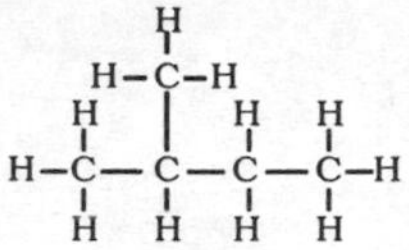

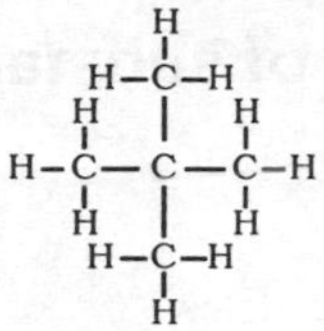

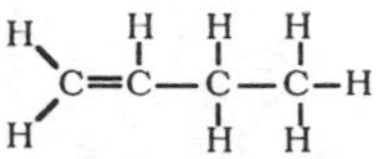

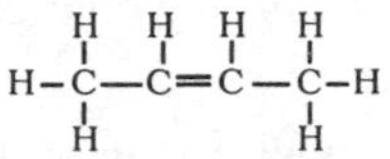

isomers

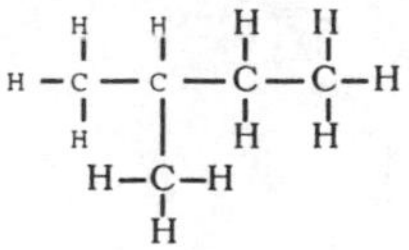

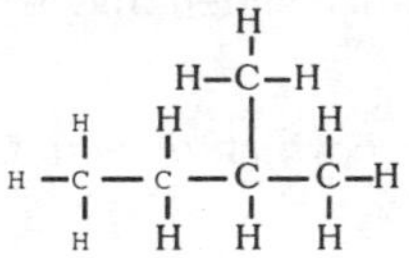

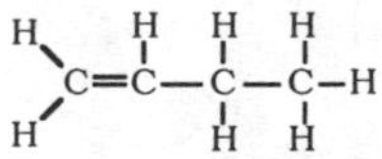

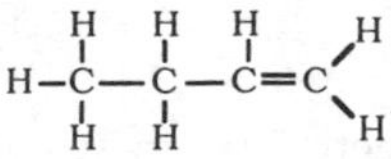

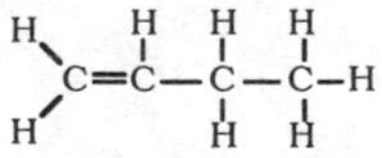

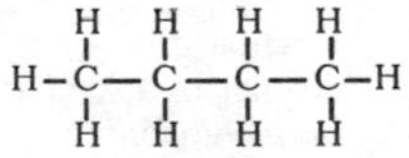

not isomers

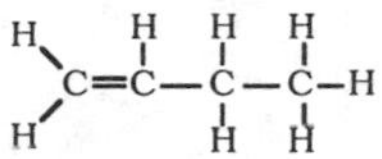

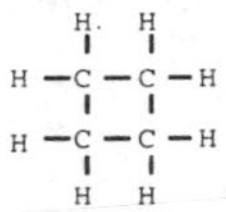

isomers

not isomers

Topic 7   Properties of substances

ELECTRICAL CONDUCTIVITY

❏ electric current is a flow of charged particles

❏ an **electrical conductor** is a substance which allows electricity to pass through it

❏ an **electrical insulator** is a substance which does not conduct electricity

❏ electrons flow through metal elements (and graphite)

❏ the movement of electrons does not chemically change an element

❏ **electrolysis** is the use of electricity to split up an ionic compound in solution or as a melt (an **electrolyte**)

❏ ions flow through electrolytes

❏ ions are not free to move in solids

❏ the movement of ions through an electrolyte causes chemical reactions to occur at the electrodes leading to the decomposition of the electrolyte

❏ a direct current (d.c.) supply must be used if the products are to be identified

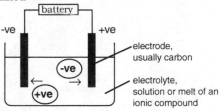

❏ negative non-metal ions are attracted to the positive electrode, losing electrons to form atoms,

e.g. $2Cl^-(aq) \rightarrow Cl_2(g) + 2e$

❏ positive metal ions are attracted to the negative electrode, gaining electrons to form atoms,

e.g. $Cu^{2+}(aq) + 2e \rightarrow Cu(s)$

❏

Solution/melt	Product at positive electrode	Product at negative electrode
copper chloride solution	chlorine	copper
lead iodide melt	iodine	lead

❑   substances can be classified in different ways

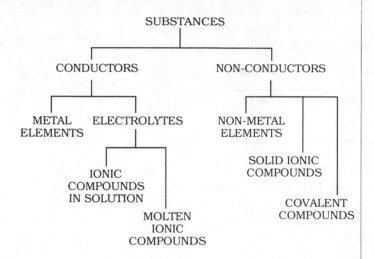

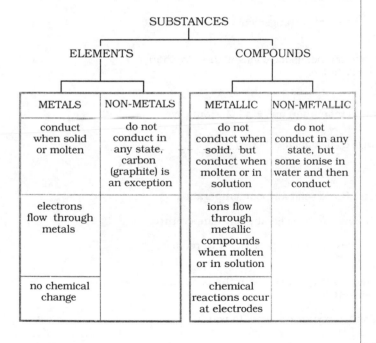

METALS	NON-METALS	METALLIC	NON-METALLIC
conduct when solid or molten	do not conduct in any state, carbon (graphite) is an exception	do not conduct when solid, but conduct when molten or in solution	do not conduct in any state, but some ionise in water and then conduct
electrons flow through metals		ions flow through metallic compounds when molten or in solution	
no chemical change		chemical reactions occur at electrodes	

IONS

❏ are charged particles formed when atoms lose or gain electrons

❏ a **crystal lattice** is a network of oppositely charged ions

❏ metal atoms lose electrons to form positive ions,
e.g.

Ion	Charge
sodium	Na^+
magnesium	Mg^{2+}
aluminium	Al^{3+}

❏ non-metal atoms gain electrons to form negative ions,
e.g.

Ion	Charge
chloride	Cl^-
oxide	O^{2-}
nitride	N^{3-}

❏ these ions have the stable arrangements of the atoms of the noble gases

❏ some of the transition metals have ions with more than one charge (see Formulae),
e.g. Cu^+, Cu^{2+}

❏ group ions contain more than one kind of atom (see Formulae),
e.g. ammonium (NH_4^+), sulphate (SO_4^{2-})

Properties

❏ all ionic compounds are solid at room temperature

❏ covalent compounds can be solid at room temperature

❏ compounds which exist as liquids or gases at room temperature are covalent

❏ ionic compounds dissolve in water with the lattice breaking up completely

❏ some covalent substances are soluble in water,
e.g. sugar

❏ covalent substances which are insoluble in water can dissolve in other solvents,
e.g. paints are soluble in turpentine, nail varnish is soluble in acetone

Colours of ionic compounds

❑ the colours of ionic compounds depend on the colours of the positive and negative ions

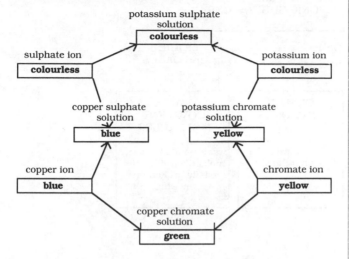

Electrolysis of copper chromate solution

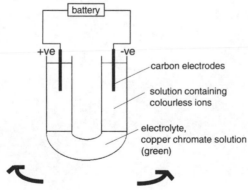

❑ movement of yellow colour towards the positive electrode;

movement of blue colour towards the negative electrode;

❑ chromate ions (negative) are attracted towards this electrode and lose electrons

copper ions (positive) are attracted towards this electrode and gain electrons

❑ ₁ substances can be classified as solids, liquids and gases

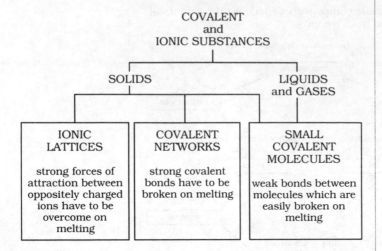

COVALENT
and
IONIC SUBSTANCES

SOLIDS

LIQUIDS
and GASES

IONIC
LATTICES

strong forces of
attraction between
oppositely charged
ions have to be
overcome on
melting

COVALENT
NETWORKS

strong covalent
bonds have to be
broken on melting

SMALL
COVALENT
MOLECULES

weak bonds between
molecules which are
easily broken on
melting

Topic 8   Acids and alkalis

pH SCALE

❑ a continuous range of numbers which indicate the acidity or alkalanity of solutions

❑ the pH number of a solution can be determined by colour matching using Universal indicator or pH paper

❑ acidic substances react with water to produce solutions with a pH less than 7

❑ acidic solutions contain more hydrogen ions, $H^+(aq)$, than pure water

❑ diluting an acidic solution decreases the concentration of $H^+(aq)$ ions and increases the pH towards 7

❑ some non-metal oxides react with water to produce acidic solutions

❑ sulphur dioxide reacts with water in the atmosphere to produce acid rain

❑ acid rain can damage buildings and can be harmful to plant and animal life,
e.g. increasing the acidity of loch-water can cause fish to die

❑ alkaline substances react with water to produce solutions with a pH greater than 7

❑ alkaline solutions contain more hydroxide ions, $OH^-(aq)$, than pure water

❑ diluting an alkaline solution decreases the concentration of $OH^-(aq)$ ions and decreases the pH towards 7

❑ some metal oxides or hydroxides react with water to produce alkaline solutions

❑ neutral solutions have a pH equal to 7

❑ pure water and neutral solutions contain a small but equal number of hydrogen ions, $H^+(aq)$, and hydroxide ions, $OH^-(aq)$

❑ pure water has a pH equal to 7

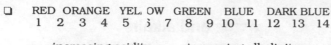

RED ORANGE YELLOW GREEN BLUE DARK BLUE
1   2   3   4   5   6   7   8   9   10 11 12 13 14

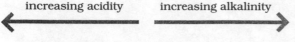

increasing acidity   increasing alkalinity

diluting an acid   diluting an alkali

decreasing concentration   decreasing concentration
of H^+(aq) ions   of OH^-(aq) ions

	Some examples of alkalis	**Some examples of acids**
found in the home	in toothpaste in indigestion powder in oven cleaner in window cleaner	as vinegar in fruit (citric acid)
from oxide	sodium hydroxide NaOH(aq) potassium hydroxide KOH(aq) calcium hydroxide Ca(OH)$_2$(aq)	sulphuric acid H_2SO_4(aq) nitric acid HNO_3(aq) carbonic acid H_2CO_3(aq) phosphoric acid H_3PO_4(aq)
not from oxide	ammonia NH_3(aq)	hydrochloric acid HCl(aq)

❏ solid sodium hydroxide and hydrogen chloride gas do not affect dry pH paper

❏ water must be present to produce OH^-(aq) ions (alkali) and H^+(aq) ions (acid):

$$Na^+OH^-(s) \xrightarrow{H_2O} Na^+(aq) \text{ and } OH^-(aq)$$
sodium hydroxide solution

$$HCl(g) \xrightarrow{H_2O} H^+(aq) \text{ and } Cl^-(aq)$$
hydrochloric acid

Topic 9   **Reactions of acids**

NEUTRALISATION

❑ is the reaction of acids with neutralisers,
   e.g. alkalis (metal hydroxides),
        metal oxides,
        metal carbonates

❑ moves the pH of an acid or alkali towards 7

❑ is the reaction of $H^+(aq)$ ions to form water

❑ produces new substances (called salts)

❑ many neutralisation reactions are important,
   e.g. addition of lime to reduce soil or lake acidity,
        treatment of acid indigestion,
        reaction of ammonia with acid to produce fertilisers in
        the chemical industry

Note

❑ metals also react with acid moving the pH towards 7

❑ in this reaction the $H^+(aq)$ ions react to form hydrogen gas,
   not water

❑ the $H^+(aq)$ ions gain electrons

$$2H^+(aq) \quad + \quad 2e \quad \rightarrow \quad H_2(g)$$

SALTS

❑ are substances in which the hydrogen ions of an acid
   have been replaced by metal ions (or ammonium ions),
   e.g. sodium chloride,
        potassium nitrate,
        ammonium sulphate

Ways of making salts

❑ salts are usually made by the reactions of acids

❑ the first part of the name is the name of the metal

❑ the second part of the name comes from the name of the
   acid

Acid		**Salt**
hydrochloric	- - - - - - - -	chloride
sulphuric	- - - - - - - -	sulphate
nitric	- - - - - - - -	nitrate

ALKALI + ACID → SALT + WATER

e.g.

sodium hydroxide + nitric acid → sodium nitrate + water

$$NaOH \quad + \quad HNO_3 \quad \rightarrow \quad NaNO_3 \quad + \quad H_2O$$

❑ an indicator has to be used to find the volume of alkali required to neutralise a known volume of acid

❑ the experiment is repeated using the same volumes without the indicator

❑ the solution is evaporated to dryness to obtain a solid sample of the product

METAL OXIDE + ACID → SALT + WATER

e.g.

zinc oxide + hydrochloric acid → zinc chloride + water

$$ZnO \quad + \quad 2HCl \quad \rightarrow \quad ZnCl_2 \quad + \quad H_2O$$

❑ an insoluble metal oxide is used

❑ the metal oxide will react with the acid but will not dissolve in the neutral solution

❑ excess metal oxide is added to the acid

❑ the unreacted metal oxide can be removed by filtering

❑ the solution (filtrate) is evaporated to dryness to obtain a solid sample of the product

METAL CARBONATE + ACID → SALT + WATER
+ CARBON DIOXIDE

e.g.

calcium carbonate + nitric acid → calcium nitrate + water
+ carbon dioxide

$$CaCO_3 \quad + \quad 2HNO_3 \quad \rightarrow \quad Ca(NO_3)_2 \quad + \quad H_2O + CO_2$$

❑ the method is the same as for an insoluble metal oxide

METAL + ACID → SALT + HYDROGEN

e.g.

zinc + sulphuric acid → zinc sulphate + hydrogen

$$Zn \quad + \quad H_2SO_4 \quad \rightarrow \quad ZnSO_4 \quad + \quad H_2$$

❑ the method is the same as for an insoluble metal oxide

ACID RAIN

Acidic gas	Where it comes from
❏ carbon dioxide	—— naturally present (respiration) increased by burning of fossil fuels
❏ sulphur dioxide	—— from power stations (burning sulphur in fossil fuels)
❏ nitrogen oxides	—— from sparking of air in petrol engines

Damage caused

❏ buildings	—— carbonates in some stone and some mortar dissolve in acid
❏ metal structures	—— steel and several other metals are dissolved by acid
❏ plants	—— most cannot grow in very acidic soils; leaves damaged by acid rain
❏ fish	—— cannot live in acidic lake or river water

PRECIPITATION

❏ is a reaction in which two solutions react to form an insoluble product,

e.g.

barium chloride solution + sodium sulphate solution

↓

barium sulphate solid + sodium chloride solution

$$BaCl_{2(aq)} \quad + \quad Na_2SO_{4(aq)} \quad \rightarrow \quad BaSO_{4(s)} \quad + \quad 2NaCl_{(aq)}$$

❏ the insoluble product is called a **precipitate**,

e.g. $BaSO_{4(s)}$

❏ the insoluble product can be removed from the solution by filtration

❏ see page 5 of the Data Booklet for a list of insoluble compounds

❏ are substances which neutralise acids,

  *e.g. alkali (metal hydroxide), metal oxide, metal carbonate,
  ammonia*

❏ an alkali is a base which is soluble in water,

  *e.g. sodium oxide dissolves in water to form sodium
  hydroxide solution (pH greater than 7)*

  $$Na_2O(s) + H_2O(l) \rightarrow 2NaOH(aq)$$

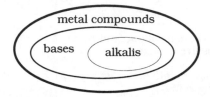

❏ an insoluble base does not affect the pH of water,

  e.g. copper(II) oxide, iron(II) carbonate

❏ the solubilities of selected bases are shown on page 5 of
  the Data Booklet

Some equations showing ions

❏ acid / alkali
  $$H^+(aq) + OH^-(aq) \rightarrow H_2O(l)$$
  (This equation applies to all acid / alkali reactions.)

❏ acid / metal oxide
  e.g.
  $$2H^+(aq) + Cu^{2+}O^{2-}(s) \rightarrow Cu^{2+}(aq) + H_2O(l)$$

❏ acid / carbonate
  e.g.
  $$2H^+(aq) + Ca^{2+}CO_3{}^{2-}(s) \rightarrow Ca^{2+}(aq) + H_2O(l) + CO_2(g)$$

❏ acid / ammonia
  $$H^+(aq) + NH_3(aq) \rightarrow NH_4{}^+(aq)$$

❏ acid / metal
  e.g.
  $$2H^+(aq) + Zn(s) \rightarrow Zn^{2+}(aq) + H_2(g)$$

❏ precipitation
  e.g.
  $$Ba^{2+}(aq) + SO_4{}^{2-}(aq) \rightarrow Ba^{2+}SO_4{}^{2-}(s)$$

Volumetric titrations

❑ experiments using a pipette and a burette can be used to find out what volume of a solution of an acid will neutralise a certain volume of a solution of an alkali

❑ an indicator is used to detect the end-point of the reaction

❑ if the concentration of one is known, the concentration of the other can be calculated (see calculations)

Topic 10   Making electricity

ELECTRICITY

❑   is a flow of charged particles
    - electrons through metal wires
    - ions through solutions and molten ionic compounds

❑   an arrangement which converts chemical energy to
    electrical energy is called a **cell**

❑   two or more cells joined together make a **battery**

❑   the two terms, cell and battery, are now interchangeable

❑   chemical reactions are used to generate electricity

❑   most batteries have to be replaced as the chemicals are
    used up in the reactions

❑   in a **rechargeable battery**, electrical energy is used to
    regenerate the chemicals so that the battery can be
    re-used,
    *e.g.   nickel/cadium cells (nicad),
            lead/acid accumulators (car batteries)*

❑   in a **dry cell**

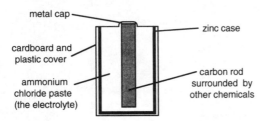

metal cap
zinc case
cardboard and plastic cover
ammonium chloride paste (the electrolyte)
carbon rod surrounded by other chemicals

    - the zinc case produces electrons (-ve terminal)
    - the carbon rod accepts electrons (+ve terminal)
    - a paste of water and ammonium chloride completes
      the circuit

❑   battery-electricity can be compared to mains-electricity

cheaper	mains
safer	battery
more portable	battery
uses fossil fuels	both

ELECTROCHEMICAL SERIES

❑ places metals in order of their ability to supply electrons

❑ two different metals (plus an electrolyte) produce a voltage when the circuit is completed

❑ different metal pairs produce different voltages

❑ metals which are far apart in the series produce higher voltages

❑ electrons flow from the metal higher in the electrochemical series to the metal lower down through the external circuit

❑ a list (**electrochemical series**) of some metals is shown on page 7 of the Data Booklet

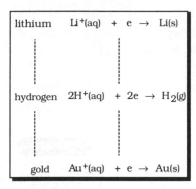

lithium $Li^+(aq)$ + e → $Li(s)$ good at supplying electrons

↑ metals react with dilute acids

hydrogen $2H^+(aq)$ + 2e → $H_2(g)$ Hydrogen is included because of the reactions of metals with dilute acids

↓ metals do not react with dilute acids

gold $Au^+(aq)$ + e → $Au(s)$ poor at supplying electrons

DISPLACEMENT

❑ is a reaction which occurs when a metal higher up in the electrochemical series is added to a solution containing ions of a metal lower down in the series

❑ the electrochemical series can be used to explain/predict observations

Zinc with copper(II) sulphate solution

❑ zinc is higher than copper in the electrochemical series

❑ zinc atoms give electrons to copper ions

❑ zinc atoms from zinc metal react to form zinc ions which dissolve into solution

❑ copper ions in solution react to form copper atoms which appear as a solid

❑ the transfer of electrons can be shown using the following cell

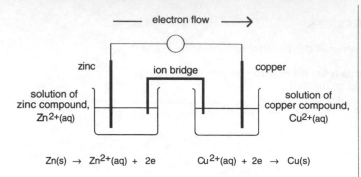

$$Zn(s) \rightarrow Zn^{2+}(aq) + 2e \qquad Cu^{2+}(aq) + 2e \rightarrow Cu(s)$$

❑ electrons flow through the meter from the metal higher in the electrochemical series to the metal lower down

❑ zinc atoms lose electrons to form zinc ions which dissolve into the solution

❑ the zinc electrode decreases in mass

❑ copper ions gain electrons to form copper atoms which appear as a solid on the electrode

❑ the copper electrode increases in mass

❑ ions move in the ion bridge to complete the circuit

REDOX REACTIONS

CREDIT

❑ involve transfer of electrons from one atom, molecule or ion to another

❑ **oxidation** is the loss of electrons by a reactant

❑ a metal element reacting to form a compound is an example of oxidation

❑ **reduction** is the gain of electrons by a reactant

❑ a compound reacting to form a metal element is an example of reduction

❑ oxidation cannot occur without reduction, and vice versa

❑ oxidation and reduction reactions can be written as ion-electron equations

❑ ion-electron equations for reduction reactions can be found on page 7 of the Data Booklet,

e.g. $Cu^{2+}(aq) + 2e \rightarrow Cu(s)$

❑ to obtain ion-electron equations for oxidation reactions, the equations in the Data Booklet must be turned round,

e.g. $Mg(s) \rightarrow Mg^{2+}(aq) + 2e$

❑ oxidation and reduction reactions need not involve metals/metal ions,

e.g. $SO_3^{2-}(aq)$ + $H_2O(l)$ → $SO_4^{2-}(aq)$ + $2H^+(aq)$ + $2e$
oxidation

$Br_2(aq)$ + $2e$ → $2Br^-(aq)$
reduction

❑ Oxidation is Loss : **OIL**

❑ Reduction is Gain : **RIG**

❑ in a test tube displacement reaction,
- atoms of the metal higher up in the electrochemical series are oxidised
- ions of the metal lower down in the series are reduced,

e.g. zinc/copper(II) sulphate solution

$Zn(s)$ → $Zn^{2+}(aq)$ + $2e$ oxidation

$Cu^{2+}(aq)$ + $2e$ → $Cu(s)$ reduction

❑ the test tube reaction between iron(III) ions, $Fe^{3+}(aq)$, and iodide ions, $I^-(aq)$, is another example of a redox reaction

❑ a cell will show the flow of electrons

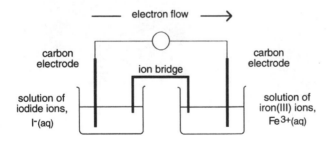

$2I^-(aq)$ → $I_2(aq)$ + $2e$ $Fe^{3+}(aq)$ + e → $Fe^{2+}(aq)$
oxidation   reduction

- during electrolysis, oxidation occurs at the positive electrode and reduction occurs at the negative electrode,

  e.g.   electrolysis of copper(II) chloride solution

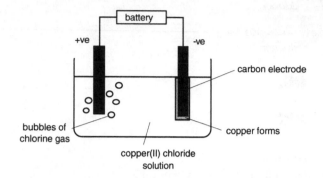

$$2Cl^-(aq) \rightarrow Cl_2(g) + 2e$$
oxidation

$$Cu^{2+}(aq) + 2e \rightarrow Cu(s)$$
reduction

Some physical properties

❏ when choosing a metal for a given purpose, cost and corrosion resistance have to be taken into account as well as relevant physical properties

Property	Statement	Application
Melting point	All metals apart from mercury are solid at room temperature.	Mercury is used in thermometers.
Density	The densities of metals vary from less than water (sodium) to very dense (lead).	Aluminium is used in aircraft because of its low density (and strength).
Thermal conductivity	All metals conduct heat well.	Aluminium and stainless steel are used for cooking pans.
Malleability	Metals can be bent into different shapes.	Car bodies are a flat sheet of steel pressed into shape.
Strength	Some metals are strong under tension.	Iron is used to make steel girders and steel to reinforce concrete.
Electrical conductivity	All metals are good conductors (as solids and liquids).	Copper and aluminium are used for electrical wiring.

REACTIVITY SERIES

❏ a list which places metals in order of their readiness to take part in chemical reactions

❏ reactive metals are at the top and unreactive (inactive) metals are at the bottom

❏ reactions with oxygen, water and dilute acid can be used to put the metals in order

❏ the order is based on observations,
e.g. speed of reactions, energy released

- the order is very similar to (but not identical to) the order in the electrochemical series

| Metal | As elements: most reactive metals at top | | | | As compounds: least reactive compounds at top |
	with oxygen	with water	with acid	with compounds	as oxides
potassium	metals which burn to form metal oxide (higher ones also burn in air at 15 °C)	metals which displace hydrogen from cold water; an alkaline solution is formed	metals too reactive to try in acid	in general each metal can displace any metal below it from one of its compounds	metal oxides do not decompose on heating with carbon or carbon monoxide; electrical energy required to decompose compounds
sodium
lithium
calcium
magnesium
aluminium			metals which displace hydrogen from acid		
zinc					metal oxides decompose on heating with carbon or carbon monoxide
iron					
nickel	metals which form oxide on the surface only				
tin					
lead					
hydrogen					
copper			metals which do not displace hydrogen from acids		
silver					metal oxides decompose on heating to form metal
mercury					
gold					

NOTE

- hydrogen is included because of the reactions of metals with dilute acids

- some metals melt before they react with oxygen

- if an unreactive metal is powdered, it may react completely with oxygen

- a good source of oxygen is potassium permanganate as shown in the diagram below

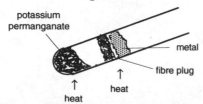

Metals as resources

❑ an **ore** is a naturally occurring compound of a metal,
e.g. iron ore contains iron oxide

❑ **extraction** involves obtaining a metal from its ore

❑ the supply of a **finite resource** is limited, i.e. it may
eventually run out

❑ metals are often **recycled**, i.e. used again, rather than
thrown away as waste

❑ metals which are found **uncombined** are not joined up
with other elements,
e.g. gold, silver

❑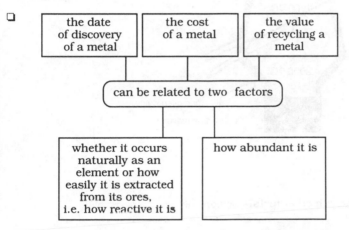

❑ silver and gold have been known since earliest civilisation
since they are very unreactive and therefore found
uncombined

❑ aluminium and magnesium were not discovered until the
nineteenth century since they are quite reactive and very
difficult to extract from their ores

❑ the cost of recycling aluminium is less than the cost of
extracting aluminium from its ore

Production of iron from iron ore

❑ in industry this is carried out in the Blast Furnace

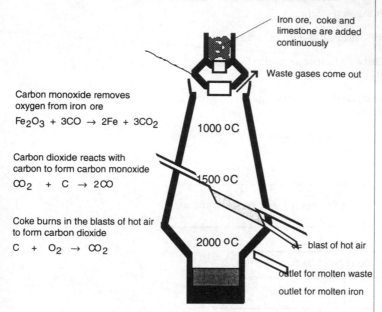

Iron ore, coke and limestone are added continuously

Waste gases come out

Carbon monoxide removes oxygen from iron ore

$$Fe_2O_3 + 3CO \rightarrow 2Fe + 3CO_2$$

1000 °C

Carbon dioxide reacts with carbon to form carbon monoxide

$$CO_2 + C \rightarrow 2CO$$

1500 °C

Coke burns in the blasts of hot air to form carbon dioxide

$$C + O_2 \rightarrow CO_2$$

2000 °C

blast of hot air

outlet for molten waste

outlet for molten iron

ALLOYS

❑ are mixtures of metals with other metals or non-metals

Alloy	Metal present	Uses
brass	copper and zinc	ornaments, hinges, doorhandles
solder	lead and tin	making electrical connections
stainless steel	iron, nickel and chronium	kitchen sinks, cutlery

Topic 12   Corrosion

CORROSION

❑ is the oxidation of metals due to the action of the weather

❑ involves the metal changing from an element to a compound

❑ involves the metal changing from atoms to ions

❑ only applies to metal materials

❑ different metals corrode at different rates

❑ in general, the more reactive the metal, the faster the process

❑ salt, spread on roads in winter, increases the rate of corrosion of car bodywork (the salt acts as an electrolyte)

❑ acid rain increases the rate of corrosion

RUSTING

❑ is the special name used for the corrosion of iron

❑ both water and oxygen (air) are required

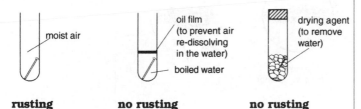

rusting   **no rusting**   **no rusting**

❑ when iron rusts, initially the iron atoms lose two electrons to form iron(II) ions, Fe^{2+}

❑ ferroxyl indicator, which turns blue in the presence of $Fe^{2+}(aq)$ ions, can be used to show the extent of the rusting process

❑ the effect of salt and acid rain on the rate of rusting can be shown

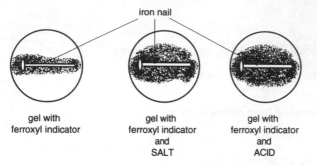

iron nail

gel with
ferroxyl indicator

gel with
ferroxyl indicator
and
SALT

gel with
ferroxyl indicator
and
ACID

- **increased intensity of blue colour**
- **more Fe^{2+}(aq) ions**
- **faster rusting**

Iron in contact with another metal

❑ electrons flowing to the iron prevent rusting

❑ with metals higher in the electrochemical series, electrons flow to the iron; with metals lower in the electrochemical series, electrons flow from the iron

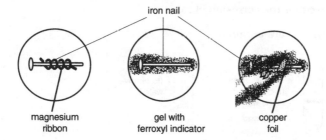

iron nail

magnesium
ribbon

gel with
ferroxyl indicator

copper
foil

- **no blue colour**
- **no rusting**

- **increased intensity of blue colour**
- **more Fe^{2+}(aq) ions**
- **faster rusting**

How to prevent rusting

Physical barrier
❑ this keeps air and water out,
   e.g. paint, grease, plastic coat, tar coat, plated metal coat
❑ since no air or water are in contact with the iron no rusting
   occurs

Electrical protection
❑ iron is connected to the negative terminal of a battery
❑ electrons flow to the iron so it does not corrode

Sacrificial protection
❑ a metal more reactive than iron is plated on or attached
❑ electrons flow from the more reactive metal to the iron;
   the more reactive metal corrodes and the iron is protected

Special examples

Galvanising
❑ iron is coated with zinc
❑ zinc acts as physical barrier
❑ if scratched, zinc provides sacrificial protection
❑ electrons flow from the more reactive zinc to the iron
❑ the zinc corrodes and the iron is protected
❑ used to protect some car bodies

Tin plating
❑ tin acts as physical barrier
❑ electrons flow from the more reactive iron to the tin
❑ if the tin layer is broken the rate of rusting is faster than
   that of iron on its own
❑ used to protect food-stuff cans (tin cans)

Electroplating
❑ electricity is used to coat iron (or steel) with another metal
❑ this coating acts as a physical barrier
❑ used in the chromium plating of bicycle parts

Using scrap magnesium
❑ scrap magnesium is attached to iron
❑ this acts as a sacrificial protector
❑ electrons flow from the more reactive magnesium to the iron
❑ the magnesium corrodes and the iron is protected
❑ used to protect underground pipes

CORROSION

❑ is an example of oxidation
$$Fe_{(s)} \rightarrow Fe^{2+}_{(aq)} + 2e$$

❑ iron(II) ions (black, early rust) can be further oxidised to give iron(III) ions (brown, main rust)
$$Fe^{2+}_{(aq)} \rightarrow Fe^{3+}_{(aq)} + e$$

❑ water, oxygen and dissolved carbon dioxide (or another electrolyte) are required for rusting

❑ electrons lost by the iron during rusting are accepted by the water and oxygen to form hydroxide ions
$$2H_2O_{(l)} + O_{2(g)} + 4e \rightarrow 4OH^-_{(aq)}$$

❑ ferroxyl indicator, which turns pink in the presence of $OH^-_{(aq)}$ ions, can be used to show the extent of the reduction

Iron/carbon cell

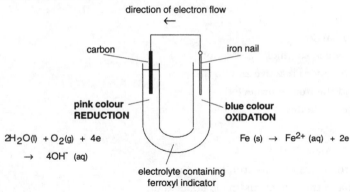

direction of electron flow
←

carbon

iron nail

**pink colour
REDUCTION**

**blue colour
OXIDATION**

$$2H_2O_{(l)} + O_{2(g)} + 4e$$
$$\rightarrow 4OH^-_{(aq)}$$

$$Fe_{(s)} \rightarrow Fe^{2+}_{(aq)} + 2e$$

electrolyte containing
ferroxyl indicator

Iron/copper cell

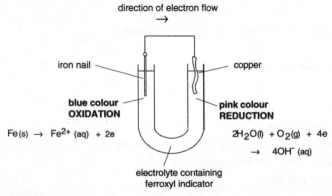

direction of electron flow
→

iron nail

copper

**blue colour
OXIDATION**

**pink colour
REDUCTION**

$$Fe_{(s)} \rightarrow Fe^{2+}_{(aq)} + 2e$$

$$2H_2O_{(l)} + O_{2(g)} + 4e$$
$$\rightarrow 4OH^-_{(aq)}$$

electrolyte containing
ferroxyl indicator

Magnesium/iron cell

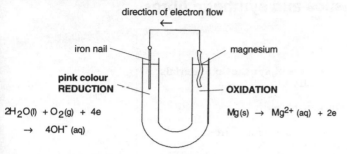

direction of electron flow

$\leftarrow$

iron nail — — magnesium

**pink colour
REDUCTION** ‐‐‐‐ **OXIDATION**

$2H_2O(l) + O_2(g) + 4e$ $Mg(s) \rightarrow Mg^{2+}(aq) + 2e$

$\rightarrow \; 4OH^-(aq)$

❏   voltmeter polarity gives the direction of electron flow - from the more reactive metal

❏   if iron is more reactive, then iron will be oxidised; with ferroxyl indicator, a blue colour will form round iron and a pink colour at the other electrode

❏   if iron is less reactive, then the other metal will be oxidised; with ferroxyl indicator no blue colour will form but a pink colour may form round the iron

Topic 13   Plastics and synthetic fibres

PLASTICS

❏ are not natural but are examples of **synthetic** materials
(made by the chemical industry)

❏ can be used to make synthetic fibres

❏ both plastics and synthetic fibres are made from
chemicals obtained from oil

❏ the uses of plastics are related to their properties

Plastic	Property	Use
PVC	flexible, non-conductor of electricity	insulating electrical cable
PVC	light, does not react with water nor acid rain	house pipes, guttering, window frames
polystyrene	light, poor conductor of heat	packaging, ceiling tiles, drinking cups
poly(ethene)	light, durable, unreactive	washing-up bottles, kitchen bowls

❏ **thermoplastics** soften on heating and can be reshaped
over and over again,

e.g. nylon , polythene

❏ **thermosetting plastics** harden on heating and do not
melt on reheating,

e.g. bakelite, formica

Plastic	Property	Use
bakelite	heat-resisitant, rigid, non-conductor of electricity	plugs, sockets
formica	rigid, heat-resistant	kitchen work-tops

❏ plastics have replaced many traditional materials

Use	Traditional material	Plastic material	Advantage of plastic material
pipes guttering,	metal	PVC	light, does not corrode
window frames	wood	PVC	does not require paint for protection
crockery	china	melamine	light, does not break but less attractive
carpets	wool	nylon, polyester	better wear but less warmth

Problems with plastics

❏ most plastics are not **biodegradable** ('bio' refers to living things and 'degradable' means able to rot away)

❏ some plastics burn or smoulder to give off toxic fumes; the fumes are related to the elements present in the plastics

Plastic	Elements	Fumes
any	C	carbon monoxide in limited air
PVC	C, H, Cl	carbon monoxide hydrogen chloride
polyurethane	C, H, N	carbon monoxide hydrogen cyanide

POLYMERS

❑ are very big molecules with a long chain of carbon atoms

❑ plastics are examples of polymers

❑ fibres, both natural and synthetic, are examples of polymers

❑ are made from smaller units called **monomers**

❑ many monomers are small unsaturated molecules produced by cracking

❑ these monomers have a carbon to carbon double covalent bond

❑ the polymers have only carbon to carbon single covalent bonds

❑ **polymerisation** is the making of a plastic (polymer) by the joining up of monomer units

Monomer	Plastic (polymer)
ethene	poly(ethene)
propene	poly(propene)
styrene	polystyrene
vinylchloride	polyvinylchloride (PVC)

❑ the ethene monomers add together by the opening of the double bonds

$$
\underset{\underset{H}{|}}{\overset{\overset{H}{|}}{C}} = \underset{\underset{H}{|}}{\overset{\overset{H}{|}}{C} } \quad + \quad \underset{\underset{H}{|}}{\overset{\overset{H}{|}}{C}} = \underset{\underset{H}{|}}{\overset{\overset{H}{|}}{C}} \quad + \quad \underset{\underset{H}{|}}{\overset{\overset{H}{|}}{C}} = \underset{\underset{H}{|}}{\overset{\overset{H}{|}}{C}} \qquad \text{ethene}
$$

↓

$$
-\overset{\overset{H}{|}}{\underset{\underset{H}{|}}{C}} - \overset{\overset{H}{|}}{\underset{\underset{H}{|}}{C}} - \overset{\overset{H}{|}}{\underset{\underset{H}{|}}{C}} - \overset{\overset{H}{|}}{\underset{\underset{H}{|}}{C}} - \overset{\overset{H}{|}}{\underset{\underset{H}{|}}{C}} - \overset{\overset{H}{|}}{\underset{\underset{H}{|}}{C}} - \qquad \text{poly(ethene)}
$$

ADDITION POLYMERS

❏ are plastics formed by the opening of the double bond in monomer units (**addition polymerisation**),

e.g. polyalkenes

$$\underset{\text{propene}}{\overset{H}{\underset{H}{\overset{CH_3}{\underset{H}{C=C}}}}} + \overset{H}{\underset{H}{\overset{CH_3}{\underset{H}{C=C}}}} + \overset{H}{\underset{H}{\overset{CH_3}{\underset{H}{C=C}}}} \rightarrow \underset{\text{poly(propene)}}{-\overset{H}{\underset{H}{C}}-\overset{CH_3}{\underset{H}{C}}-\overset{H}{\underset{H}{C}}-\overset{CH_3}{\underset{H}{C}}-\overset{H}{\underset{H}{C}}-\overset{CH_3}{\underset{H}{C}}-}$$

$$\underset{\text{polyvinyl chloride}}{-\overset{H}{\underset{Cl}{C}}-\overset{H}{\underset{H}{C}}-\overset{H}{\underset{Cl}{C}}-\overset{H}{\underset{H}{C}}-\overset{H}{\underset{Cl}{C}}-\overset{H}{\underset{H}{C}}-} \qquad \text{formed from} \qquad \underset{\text{vinyl chloride}}{\overset{H}{\underset{Cl}{\overset{H}{\underset{H}{C=C}}}}}$$

FERTLISERS

❏   restore essential elements for plant growth (**nutrients**)

❏   these elements include nitrogen, phosphorus and potassium

❏   different crops need different proportions of nitrogen, phosphorus and potassium

❏   fertilisers contain compounds of the essential elements, *e.g. nitrate, phosphate, ammonium and potassium compounds*

❏   more efficient food production is required to meet the needs of the increasing world population

❏   converting atmospheric nitrogen to nitrogen compounds is called **nitrogen fixation**

❏   fertilisers must be soluble so that they can be taken in by plants through the roots

❏   fertilisers which are very soluble can be washed away by rain-water into rivers and lochs - this can be harmful to fish-life

❏   **synthetic** fertilisers are made in the chemical industry by the Haber and Ostwald Processes (see later)

❏   **natural** fertilisers are made by the bacterial decomposition of plant remains (compost) and animal remains (manure)

❏   bacterial methods of fixing nitrogen are cheaper than chemical methods

AMMONIA

❏   is the name given to nitrogen hydride

❏   has the chemical formula NH_3

❏   is a colourless gas with a 'smelling salts' smell

❏   is very soluble in water, producing an alkaline solution (a gas which turns damp pH paper and Universal indicator blue is likely to be ammonia)

$$NH_{3(g)} + H_2O_{(l)} \rightarrow NH_4^+{}_{(aq)} + OH^-{}_{(aq)}$$

❏ reacts with acids to form ammonium compounds (see later)

❏ the catalytic oxidation of ammonia is the industrial route to nitric acid (see later)

NITROGEN CYCLE

❏ the energy associated with lightning or the spark in a car engine results in nitrogen reacting with oxygen to form nitrogen dioxide gas

$$N_2(g) \;+\; 2O_2(g) \;\;\rightarrow\;\; 2NO_2(g)$$

❏ this non-metal oxide dissolves in rain water providing a source of nitrogen for plants but contributing to the acid rain problem

❏ nitrifying bacteria in the root nodules of some plants can convert atmospheric nitrogen into nitrogen compounds, *e.g. bean, pea, clover*

❏

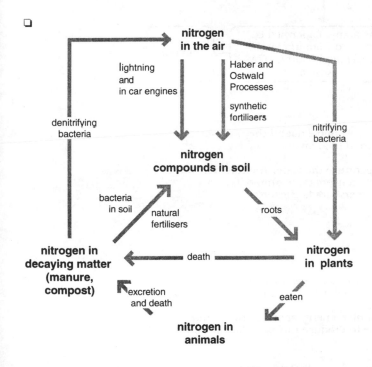

The industrial manufacture of ammonia

❑ this is known as the **Haber Process**

$$N_2(g) \quad + \quad 3H_2(g) \rightleftharpoons 2NH_3(g)$$

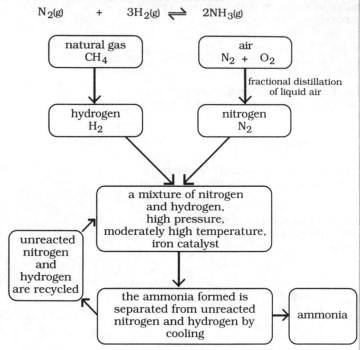

❑ since the reaction is reversible not all the nitrogen and hydrogen are converted to ammonia

❑ the higher the temperature the faster the rate but the lower the percentage conversion to ammonia, so a moderately high temperature is chosen

Sparking of air

❑ due to the energy required to break triple bonds in the molecules, nitrogen is not a very reactive gas

❑ in the presence of a high energy spark nitrogen and oxygen can combine to produce nitrogen dioxide, a brown gas

$$N_2(g) \quad + \quad 2O_2(g) \quad \rightarrow \quad 2NO_2(g)$$

❑ the gas dissolves in water to produce an acidic solution (nitric acid)

❑ this reaction takes place in the atmosphere during lightning conditions and at the spark-plugs in car engines

❑ due to the energy involved in the reaction, it does not provide an economical industrial route to nitric acid

The catalytic oxidation of ammonia

❑ this is the industrial route to nitric acid

❑ this route is known as the **Ostwald Process**

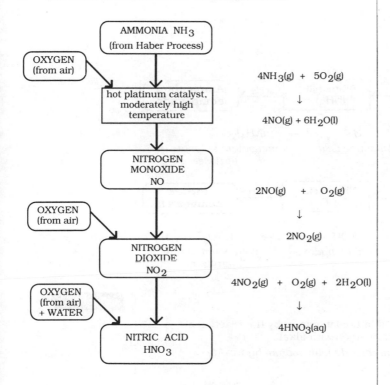

$$4NH_3(g) + 5O_2(g)$$

$$\downarrow$$

$$4NO(g) + 6H_2O(l)$$

$$2NO(g) + O_2(g)$$

$$\downarrow$$

$$2NO_2(g)$$

$$4NO_2(g) + O_2(g) + 2H_2O(l)$$

$$\downarrow$$

$$4HNO_3(aq)$$

❑ since the reaction is exothermic (heat is given out) there is no need to keep heating once the reaction has started

❑ as with the Haber Process, the higher the temperature the faster the rate of reaction but the lower the percentage conversion, so a moderately high temperature is chosen

❑ the catalytic oxidation of ammonia can also be carried out in the laboratory

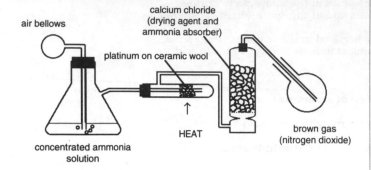

Making fertilisers

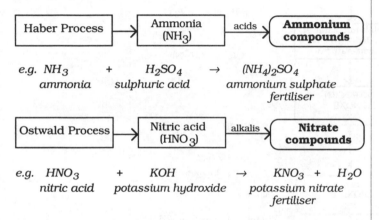

e.g. NH_3 + H_2SO_4 → $(NH_4)_2SO_4$
    ammonia   sulphuric acid   ammonium sulphate
                                              fertiliser

e.g. HNO_3 + KOH → KNO_3 + H_2O
    nitric acid   potassium hydroxide   potassium nitrate
                                                   fertiliser

AMMONIA

❏   can be prepared in the laboratory by the reaction of
    ammonium compounds with alkali,

    e.g. *ammonium chloride with sodium hydroxide*

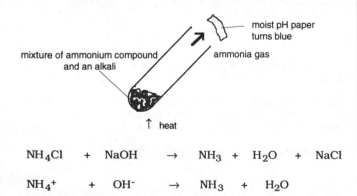

NH_4Cl + $NaOH$ → NH_3 + H_2O + $NaCl$

NH_4^+ + OH^- → NH_3 + H_2O

Topic 15   Carbohydrates

PHOTOSYNTHESIS

- ❑ is the process by which plants make glucose from carbon dioxide and water

- ❑ light energy is required

- ❑ plants require chlorophyll to absorb light

- ❑ oxygen is released in the process

- ❑ the energy is stored as chemical energy in the plants

- ❑ plants are an important source of energy-foods for animals

RESPIRATION

- ❑ is the process by which animals (and plants) obtain a supply of energy by breaking down glucose

- ❑ oxygen is used in the process

- ❑ carbon dioxide and water are released

- ❑ energy is used for warmth, movement, etc.

CARBON CYCLE

❑

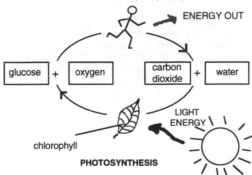

- ❑ the processes of photosynthesis and respiration are important in maintaining the balance of carbon dioxide and oxygen in the air, **BUT**

- ❑ (i) the burning of fossil fuels contributes to an increase in levels of carbon dioxide

❑ (ii) extensive burning of forest areas contributes to an increase in levels of carbon dioxide

❑ (iii) the clearing of forests can reduce the rate of photosynthesis (which removes carbon dioxide)

CARBOHYDRATES

❑ contain the elements carbon, hydrogen and oxygen,
   e.g. glucose and starch

	GLUCOSE	STARCH
Taste	sweet	not sweet
Solubility	dissolves in water	does not dissolve well in water
Effect on beam of light	not reflected	reflected
Test	use Benedict's solution (or Fehling's solution)	use iodine solution
	heat on a water bath	no heat required
	turns yellow/orange/ red/brown	turns blue/black
Size	small molecules	large molecules

polymerisation
in plants

monomer ———————→ polymer
        ←———————
        digestion
(breakdown in the gut; glucose molecules
are small enough to pass through the gut wall
into the bloodstream to be used in respiration)

❑ burn in the laboratory producing carbon dioxide (CO_2) and water (H_2O) and releasing energy (see Respiration)

ENZYMES

❑ are biological catalysts

❑ control the breakdown of complex food molecules into smaller ones in the digestive system,
   e.g. amylase controls the breakdown of starch

FERMENTATION

❑ is the breakdown of glucose to form alcohol

❑ carbon dioxide is produced in the process

❑ an enzyme in yeast, a living organism, acts as a catalyst for the reaction

❑ alcoholic drinks can be made from any fruit or vegetable which is a source of starch or sugars

❑ the type of alcoholic drink varies with the plant source of the carbohydrate

Source	Drink
grape	wine
barley	beer, whisky
apples	cider
potatoes	vodka

❑ at concentrations above about 15% the alcohol poisons the living organisms in the yeast

❑ there is therefore a limit to the alcohol concentration of fermentation products

DISTILLATION

❑ is a method of increasing the alcohol concentration of fermentation products

❑ water and alcohol can be separated by distillation because of the difference in boiling points

❑ alcohol (bp 78 $^{\circ}$C) boils off first

❑ the process can be carried out in the laboratory

❑ different drinks have a different alcohol content

Drink	Alcohol content
beer	4%
wine	10%
spirits	40%

ALCOHOL

❑ is a member of the alkanol family

❑ the alcohol produced by fermentation is called ethanol

❑ is a sedative and slows down the nervous system; this can lead to loss of control and balance and unconsciousness; death can result

❑ long term abuse can cause cirrhosis of the liver

Burning of carbohydrates

CREDIT

❑ the production of water (H_2O) indicates that hydrogen must be present

❑ the production of carbon dioxide (CO_2) indicates that carbon must be present

❑ these products do not show the presence of oxygen since the oxygen of the air reacts with a carbohydrate on burning

❑

MONOSACCHARIDES	DISACCHARIDES	POLYSACCHARIDES
$C_6H_{12}O_6$	$C_{12}H_{22}O_{11}$	$(C_6H_{10}O_5)_n$
monomer	dimer	polymer
glucose and fructose are isomers	sucrose and maltose are isomers	starch
both reduce Benedict's solution (or Fehling's solution)	only maltose reduces Benedict's solution (or Fehling's solution)	iodine solution test is specific to starch

CONDENSATION POLYMERISATION

❑ is the joining up of small molecules (monomers) to form large molecules (polymers) with the loss of water,

e.g. the joining up of glucose molecules to form starch

HO—[G]—OH HO—[G]—OH HO—[G]—OH HO—[G]—OH

glucose

↓

starch   —O—[G]—O—[G]—O—[G]—O—[G]—O—   + H_2O

HYDROLYSIS

❏ is the breaking up of large molecules by the addition of the elements from water molecules,

   e.g. breaking up of starch by the reaction with water

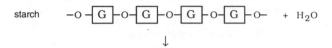

starch $-O\boxed{G}O\boxed{G}O\boxed{G}O\boxed{G}O-$ + H_2O

   ↓

HO$\boxed{G}$OH   HO$\boxed{G}$OH   HO$\boxed{G}$OH   HO$\boxed{G}$OH

glucose

   e.g. the breaking up of sucrose by the reaction with water

HO$\boxed{G}O\boxed{F}$OH + H_2O → HO$\boxed{G}$OH   HO$\boxed{F}$OH

   sucrose   glucose   fructose

Optimum efficiency

❏ the efficiency of enzymes are affected by changes in pH and temperature

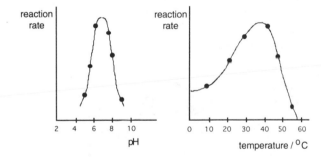

❏ the enzyme is most efficient, i.e. rate is fastest, under optimum conditions

❏ this particular enzyme has an optimum pH of 7 and an optimum temperature of 37 °C

❏ optimum pH values and optimum temperatures vary from one enzyme to another

❏ enzymes in the human body have an optimum temperature of about 37 °C

Formulae

Stable electron arrangements

❏ the noble gases are **unreactive** elements

❏ atoms of these elements have **filled outer energy levels**

❏ helium has 2 electrons in the outer energy level

❏ neon, argon, krypton and xenon have 8 electrons in the outer energy levels

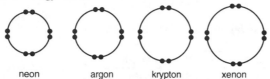

      neon   argon   krypton   xenon

❏ atoms which are bonded together tend to have the same electron arrangements as atoms of the nearest noble gases

❏ only electrons in the outer energy levels are involved in bonding

❏ with **covalent bonding** the stable electron arrangements are achieved by the sharing of pairs of electrons between atoms

Example   **nitrogen hydride (ammonia)**

    H   N NH_3

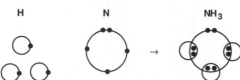

❏ the number of bonds which an atom forms is equal to the number of "extra" electrons which an atom requires to reach the same electron arrangement as a noble gas

	C	N	O	F	Ne
	Si	P	S	Cl	Ar
Number of outer electrons	4	5	6	7	8
Number of extra electrons	4	3	2	1	0
Number of bonds formed	4	3	2	1	0

- the atom of hydrogen needs 1 electron to reach the same electron arrangement as an atom of helium; hence hydrogen forms 1 bond

- it is easier for atoms of elements in Groups 1 to 3 to lose electrons to reach noble gas electron arrangements; this explains why atoms of metal elements do not form covalent bonds

- with **ionic bonding** the stable electron arrangement is achieved by the tranfer of electrons between atoms

Example   magnesium chloride

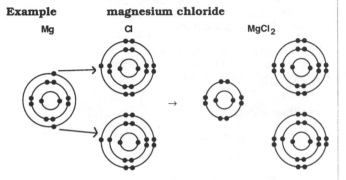

Mg   Cl   MgCl$_2$

Writing formulae - covalent compounds

- covalent compounds (usually) are made up of atoms of non-metal elements

Example   carbon fluoride

Step 1   Use the Periodic Table to write symbols for the elements

C   F

Step 2   Use the Periodic Table to put in the number of bonds which will be formed by each atom

$-\overset{|}{\underset{|}{C}}-$ $-F$

Step 3   Complete the bonding picture

$$F-\overset{\overset{\displaystyle F}{|}}{\underset{\underset{\displaystyle F}{|}}{C}}-F$$

Step 4   Write the formula CF$_4$

- the formula of some covalent compounds are indicated by the names; do not use bonding pictures for these compounds,
  e.g. *carbon monoxide (CO); sulphur dioxide (SO$_2$)*

Writing formulae - ionic compounds

(i) Simple ionic compounds

❑ the charge on many ions can be worked out from the electron arrangements on page 1 of the Data Booklet

group 1	group 2	group 3	group 4	group 5	group 6	group 7	group 8
1+	2+	3+		3-	2-	1-	

❑ in an ionic compound, the charge on all positive ions must balance the charge on all negative ions

❑ since the overall charge is neutral, the formula for an ionic compound can be worked out by finding the relative number of each ion required to make the over-all charge zero

Example 1   sodium chloride

positive ion   negative ion

Na^+ Cl^-

formula Na^+Cl^- or $NaCl$

Example 2   potassium oxide

positive ion   negative ion

K^+ O^{2-}

formula $(K^+)_2O^{2-}$ or K_2O

(ii) Elements with ions which show variable charge

❑ some metals have ions with more than one charge; in compounds of these metals the charge is shown in Roman numerals after the name of the metal element,
e.g.
in iron(II) oxide the charge of the iron is two-positive (Fe^{2+})
in copper(I) oxide the charge of the copper is one-positive (Cu^+)

Example   copper(I) oxide

positive ion   negative ion

Cu^+ O^{2-}

formula $(Cu^+)_2O^{2-}$ or Cu_2O

(iii) Group ions

❑ a number of ions consist of a group of atoms which tend to stay together during reactions; these are called **group ions**

❑ the charge is on the whole group and not on any particular atom,

e.g. the sulphate ion

the charge of the ion is 2-

formula for the ion

❑ the formula and charge of a group ion can be found on page 6 of the Data Booklet

❑ the presence of a group ion can usually be recognised from the -ate or -ite name ending which indicates the presence of oxygen

❑ the exceptions are the ammonium ion and the hydroxide ion

❑ apart from the ammonium ion, which has a positive charge like the metal ions, all the group ions have a negative charge

Example 1   **sodium nitrate**

positive ion   negative ion

Na^+ NO_3^-

formula $Na^+(NO_3^-)$ or $Na^+NO_3^-$ or $NaNO_3$

Note: Always put the formula for the group ion in brackets. When the subscript numeral for the group is 1, as above, the brackets can be removed. When the subscript numeral for the group is greater than 1, brackets are essential.

Example 2   **calcium nitrate**

positive ion   negative ion

Ca^{2+} NO_3^-

formula $Ca^{2+}(NO_3^-)_2$ or $Ca(NO_3)_2$

Note: The formula for calcium nitrate is $Ca^{2+}(NO_3^-)_2$ and not $Ca^{2+}NO_3^-{}_2$
The formula has one calcium ion for every two nitrate ions. This gives a total of one calcium atom, two nitrogen atoms and six oxygen atoms.

Writing formulae - using combining powers (valency)

❏ the chemical formula for a compound can always be worked out by considering the bonding; there is, however, a shorter method which uses the combining powers (valency); this method works for both covalent and ionic compounds

❏ the combining power can be found from the Periodic Table

group 1	group 2	group 3	group 4	group 5	group 6	group 7
1	2	3	4	3	2	1

❏ for metals which show variable charge the combining power corresponds to the charge on the ion,

e.g.
in iron(II) oxide the combining power of the iron ion is 2;
in copper(I) oxide the combining power of the copper ion is 1

❏ for group ions, the combining power corresponds to the charge on the ion,
e.g.
in SO_4^{2-} the combining power of the ion is 2;

in NO_3^- the combining power of the ion is 1

❏ this method will always give the correct answer, but it does not show you why it is correct; use in emergency when all else fails!

Example 1   hydrogen sulphide

Step 1   Write atoms and combining powers in this form

$$\begin{array}{cc} 1 & 2 \\ H & S \end{array}$$

Step 2   Exchange the combining powers

$$\begin{array}{cc} 1 & 2 \\ H & S \end{array}$$

Step 3   Ignore the number 1 to give the correct chemical formula

$$H_2S$$

Example 2   potassium sulphate

Step 1   As before

$$\begin{array}{cc} 1 & 2 \\ K & SO_4 \end{array}$$

Step 2   As before

$$\begin{array}{cc} 1 & 2 \\ K & SO_4 \end{array}$$

Step 3   As before

$$K_2SO_4$$

An extra step is sometimes necessary.

Example 3   silicon oxide

Step 1   As before

$$\overset{4}{Si} \quad \overset{2}{O}$$

Step 2   Cancel the numbers 2 and 4
              to give 1 and 2

$$\overset{2}{Si} \diagdown \overset{1}{O}$$

Step 3   As step 2 before

$$\overset{2}{Si} \diagdown \overset{1}{O}$$

Step 4   As step 3 before

$$SiO_2$$

State symbols

❑   suffixes can be used after the name or formula to show
     the chemical state of the substances

Suffix	Meaning
(s)	solid
(l)	liquid
(g)	gas
(aq)	dissolved in water

Example

The word equation for the burning of hydrogen is:

hydrogen gas + oxygen gas → liquid water

The word equation with state symbols is:

hydrogen (g)   +   oxygen (g)   →   water (l)

or,   using symbols and formulae:

$$2H_2(g) \quad + \quad O_2(g) \quad \rightarrow \quad 2H_2O(l)$$

Equations

❑ in a chemical reaction, substances present at the start change to make new substances

❑ the chemical reaction can be written in a short-hand form, called a **word equation**,

e.g.

> STARTING SUBSTANCE **A** + STARTING SUBSTANCE **B**
>
> ↓
>
> NEW SUBSTANCE **C** + NEW SUBSTANCE **D**

OR

> STARTING SUBSTANCE **K** → NEW SUBSTANCE **L** + NEW SUBSTANCE **M**

OR

> STARTING SUBSTANCE **X** + STARTING SUBSTANCE **Y**
>
> ↓
>
> NEW SUBSTANCE **Z**

❑ the starting substances in chemical reactions are called the **reactants**; the new substances which are produced are called the **products**

❑ in a word equation:

(i) the '**+**' sign means '**and**'
(ii) the '**→**' sign means '**changed into**'
(iii) the **reactants** come **in front** of the arrow; the **products** come **after** the arrow

Example

Here is a chemical reaction from everyday life.

The food in our bodies joins up with oxygen taken from the air to produce water vapour and carbon dioxide which we breathe out.

The word equation is:

food + oxygen → water vapour + carbon dioxide
 the reactants   **the products**

Equations using symbols and formulae

❑ an equation using symbols and formulae gives more information than a word equation - it shows the elements involved and the way in which they are joined up in the reactant(s) and product(s)

Example

The word equation for the burning of natural gas is:

natural gas + oxygen → carbon dioxide + water

This equation can be written using the formula for each reactant and product:

$$CH_4 + O_2 → CO_2 + H_2O$$

❑ in a reaction the atoms which take part (either as an element or as part of a compound) also make up what is formed

❑ the following flow diagram can be used when writing equations; it should be followed for each substance in the equation in turn

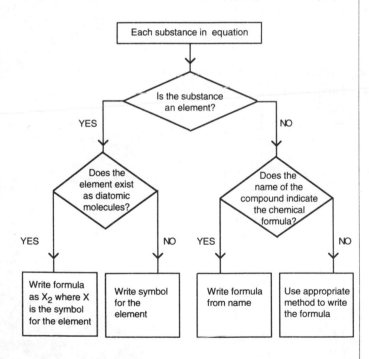

Balanced chemical equations

❑ the number of atoms (or ions) on the reactant side is equal to the number of atoms (or ions) on the product side

Example

The balanced chemical equation for the burning of magnesium is:

$$2Mg \; + \; O_2 \; \rightarrow \; 2MgO$$

❑ equations can only be balanced by putting a number in front of symbols and formulae,

e.g. **2Mg** *or* **2MgO**

❑ never change a formula to make an equation balance,

e.g. the formula for carbon dioxide is always CO_2 (CO is carbon monoxide, a quite different gas); the formula for water is always H_2O (HO does not exist)

❑ the following example shows a method of balancing equations

Example $N_2 \; + \; H_2 \; \rightarrow \; NH_3$

N	+	H	→	NH
N		H		H
				H

Two nitrogens are required on the product side.

N	+	H	→	NH
N		H		H
				H

NH
H
H

Six hydrogens are required on the reactant side.

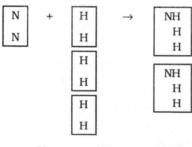

$$N_2 \; + \; 3H_2 \; \rightarrow \; 2NH_3$$

Ion-electron equations

❏ oxidation and reduction reactions are written as ion-electron equations

❏ a list of ion-electron equations is found on page 7 of the Data Booklet

❏ reduction reactions are copied as they are written in the Data Booklet,

e.g. $Cl_2(aq) + 2e \rightarrow 2Cl^-(aq)$

❏ the ion-electron equations must be turned round for oxidation reactions,

e.g. $Mg(s) \rightarrow Mg^{2+}(aq) + 2e$

Ionic equations

❏ spectator ions are ions which do not take part in chemical reactions

❏ ionic equations show only the ions which are involved in the reactions, i.e. the spectator ions are omitted

Example 1
$NaOH(aq) + HCl(aq) \rightarrow NaCl(aq) + H_2O(l)$

$Na^+(aq) + OH^-(aq) + H^+(aq) + Cl^-(aq)$
$\rightarrow Na^+(aq) + Cl^-(aq) + H_2O(l)$

ionic equation $OH^-(aq) + H^+(aq) \rightarrow H_2O(l)$

Example 2
$Mg(s) + 2HCl(aq) \rightarrow MgCl_2(aq) + H_2(g)$

$Mg(s) + 2H^+(aq) + 2Cl^-(aq)$
$\rightarrow Mg^{2+}(aq) + 2Cl^-(aq) + H_2(g)$

ionic equation $Mg(s) + 2H^+(aq) \rightarrow Mg^{2+}(aq) + H_2(g)$

Example 3
$BaCl_2(aq) + Na_2SO_4(aq) \rightarrow BaSO_4(s) + 2NaCl(aq)$

$Ba^{2+}(aq) + 2Cl^-(aq) + 2Na^+(aq) + SO_4^{2-}(aq)$
$\rightarrow (Ba^{2+} + SO_4^{2-})(s) + 2Na^+(aq) + 2Cl^-(aq)$

ionic equation $Ba^{2+}(aq) + SO_4^{2-}(aq) \rightarrow (Ba^{2+}SO_4^{2-})(s)$

Chemical calculations

FORMULA MASS

❑ the mass of an atom is measured on the atomic mass scale and the basic unit is the atomic mass unit (amu)

❑ the mass of a 'unit' of a compound is called the formula mass

❑ the formula mass is obtained by adding together all the atomic masses of the atoms (or ions) in the formula

❑ the unit given to the formula mass is the amu

Example

What is the formula mass of sodium carbonate?

Step 1	Write the formula	Na_2CO_3	*you have to work this out*
Step 2	Find the atomic masses	Na C O 23 12 16	*use the Data Booklet*
Step 3	Multiply by the number of atoms	23x2 12x1 16x3	*check with the formula*
Step 4	Do the sum	46 + 12 + 48	*calculator?*
Step 5	The answer	**106 amu**	*check it!*

THE MOLE

❑ one mole of any substance is defined as the formula mass in grams, i.e. the gram formula mass

❑ the formula mass of any substance is first calculated from the formula

❑ to calculate the mass of one mole of the substance, simply change the units to grams

Example 1

What is the mass of one mole of sodium?

Step 1	Symbol	Na
Step 2	Find the atomic mass	23 amu
Step 3	Change units to grams	**23 g**

Example 2

What is the mass of one mole of sodium sulphate?

Step 1	Write the formula		Na_2SO_4	
Step 2	Find the atomic masses	Na 23	S 32	O 16
Step 3	Multiply by the number of atoms	23x2	32x1	16x4
Step 4	Do the sum		46 + 32 + 64	
Step 5	Formula mass		142 amu	
Step 6	Change units to grams		**142 g**	

THE MOLE - FURTHER EXAMPLES

Example 1

What is the mass of two moles of sodium chloride?

Step 1	Write the formula	NaCl	
Step 2	Find the atomic masses	Na 23	Cl 35.5
Step 3	Multiply by the number of atoms	23x1	35.5x1
Step 4	Do the sum	23 + 35.5	
Step 5	Formula mass	58.5 amu	
Step 6	Change units to grams	58.5 g	
Step 7	Complete calculation	1 mol $\leftrightarrow$ 58.5 g	
		2 mol $\leftrightarrow$ **117 g**	

❏ the $\leftrightarrow$ symbol is used to show a simple proportion

Example 2

How many moles are there in 36 g of water?

Step 1	Write the formula		H_2O		
Step 2	Find the atomic masses		H 1	O 16	
Step 3	Multiply by the number of atoms		1x2	16x1	
Step 4	Do the sum		2 +	16	
Step 5	Formula mass		18 amu		
Step 6	Change units to grams		18 g		
		18 g	$\leftrightarrow$	1 mol	
Step 7	Complete calculation	36 g	$\leftrightarrow$	**2 mol**	

EMPIRICAL FORMULA

❏ this the simplest ratio of the moles of atoms of each element in a compound

Example 1

1.2 g of magnesium burned to form 2.0 g of magnesium oxide. What is the empirical formula for this oxide?

		magnesium	oxygen	
Step 1	Reacting masses	1.2 g	0.8 g	*from question*
Step 2	Relative atomic masses	24	16	*use the Data Booklet*
Step 3	Relative number of moles of each	$\dfrac{1.2}{24}$ = 0.05	$\dfrac{0.8}{16}$ = 0.05	*use calculator to work this out*
Step 4	Whole number ratio (divide previous line by the smaller number)	$\dfrac{0.05}{0.05}$ = 1	$\dfrac{0.05}{0.05}$ = 1	*if answers not close to whole numbers, try multipling by 2 or 3*
Step 5	The answer	**MgO**		

NOTE : If you are told the formula mass, you can then find the chemical formula

Example

The empirical formula is CH_2 and the formula mass is given as 56 amu.

CH_2 = 14 amu $\dfrac{56}{14}$ = 4   formula is C_4H_8

Example 2

Analysis of aluminium oxide gave the following results:
mass of aluminium = 22.5 g;   mass of oxygen = 20 g
What is the empirical formula for this oxide?

		aluminium	oxygen	
Step 1	Reacting masses	22.5 g	20 g	*from question*
Step 2	Relative atomic masses	27	16	*use the Data Booklet*
Step 3	Relative number of moles of each	$\dfrac{22.5}{27}$	$\dfrac{20}{16}$	*use calculator to work this out*
		= 0.833	= 1.25	
Step 4	Whole number ratio (divide previous line by the smaller number)	$\dfrac{0.833}{0.833}$	$\dfrac{1.25}{0.833}$	
		= 1	= 1.51	
		= 2	= 3	*multipling by 2*
Step 5	The answer		Al_2O_3	

PERCENTAGE COMPOSITION (BY MASS)

❏   this is the percentage (by mass) of each element in a compound

Example

What is the percentage composition (by mass) of copper(II) sulphate?

Step 1	Formula	$CuSO_4$	
Step 2	Formula mass	160 amu	
Step 3(a)	Percentage of copper	$\dfrac{\text{Mass of copper in copper(II) sulphate}}{\text{Formula mass of copper(II) sulphate}}$ x 100	
		$= \dfrac{64}{160}$ x 100	= 40%
Step 3(b)	Percentage of sulphur	$= \dfrac{32}{160}$ x 100	= 20%
Step 3(c)	Percentage of oxygen	$= \dfrac{4\times16}{160}$ x 100	= 40%
Step 4	Check total		100%

CONCENTRATION

❑ the concentration of an aqueous solution is the amount of solute dissolved in a certain volume of water

❑ this is usually expressed as grams per litre, g/l

❑ in chemistry, the concentration is often expressed in terms of the number of moles of the solute in 1 litre of water, i.e. mol/l

❑ a solution labelled 1 mol/l contains one mole of solute in one litre of solution

❑ a solution labelled 2 mol/l contains two moles of solute in one litre of solution

USING CONCENTRATION

Example 1

How many moles are there in 100 cm^3 of sodium hydroxide solution, concentration 0.4 mol/l?

0.4 mol/l is 0.4 mol in a litre

1000 cm^3 $\leftrightarrow$ 0.4 mol

100 cm^3 $\leftrightarrow$ **0.04 mol**

Example 2

What is the concentration of a solution of hydrochloric acid containing 0.1 mol in 50 cm^3?

50 cm^3 $\leftrightarrow$ 0.1 mol

1000 cm^3 $\leftrightarrow$ 2 mol

concentration is **2 mol/l**

Example 3

What volume of a sodium carbonate solution, concentration 2 mol/l, contains 0.5 mol?

2 mol/l is 2 mol in a litre

2 mol $\leftrightarrow$ 1000 cm^3

0.5 mol $\leftrightarrow$ **250 cm^3**

Example 4

What is the concentration of a solution of 2 g sodium hydroxide in 50 cm^3 solution?

Step 1	Formula	NaOH
Step 2	Mass of one mole	40 g
Step 3	Number of moles	$\dfrac{2}{40}$
		= 0.05
Step 4	Concentration	50 cm^3 ↔ 0.05 mol
		1000 cm^3 ↔ 1 mol
		= 1 mol/l

Example 5

How many grams of calcium chloride are there in 25 cm^3 of a solution, concentration 0.1 mol/l ?

Step 1	Formula	CaCl$_2$
Step 2	Mass of one mole	111 g
Step 3	Number of moles	1000 cm^3 ↔ 0.1 mol
		25 cm^3 ↔ 0.0025 mol
Step 4	Multiply by mass of one mole	0.0025 x 111
		= 0.2775 g

CALCULATIONS BASED ON EQUATIONS

❑ a balanced equation can be taken to give the **relative number of moles** of each reactant and product

❑ since the mass of one mole of any substance is expressed in grams, the masses involved can then be calculated

Example 1

Calculate the mass of water produced on burning 1 g of methane.

Step 1	Balanced equation	$CH_4 + 2O_2 \rightarrow CO_2 + 2H_2O$

Step 2	Relative number of moles	1 mol	2 mol

❑ it is not necessary to calculate the masses of carbon dioxide and oxygen - these substances are not included in the question

		CH_4	$2H_2O$
Step 3	Find the formula masses	$12 + (4 \times 1)$ $= 16$ amu	$2[(2 \times 1) + 16)]$ $= 36$ amu
Step 4	Mass in grams	16 g	36 g
Step 5	Complete calculation	16 g $\leftrightarrow$ 36 g 1 g $\leftrightarrow$ $\dfrac{36 \times 1}{16}$	

$$= \mathbf{2.25\ g}$$

❑ the last part of the calculation is a simple proportion and hence the use of the symbol $\leftrightarrow$

Example 2

An industrial plant produces ammonia by the Haber Process.

An output of 7.5×10^3 kg of ammonia is required each day.

Calculate the mass of nitrogen used each day.

Step 1	Balanced equation	N_2	$+$	$3H_2$	$\rightarrow$	$2NH_3$

Step 2	Relative number of moles	1 mol		2 mol

Step 3	Find the formula masses	2×14	$2[14 + (3 \times 1)]$ amu
		$= 28$ amu	$= 34$ amu

Step 4	Mass in grams	28 g	$= 34$ g

Step 5   Complete calculation

$$28 \text{ g} \quad \leftrightarrow \quad 34 \text{ g}$$

$$\frac{28 \times 7.5 \times 10^3}{34} \quad \leftrightarrow \quad 7.5 \times 10^3 \text{ g}$$

$= 6.18 \times 10^3$ kg

Example 3

Calculate the volume of hydrochloric acid, concentration 2 mol/l, which will neutralise 20 cm^3 of sodium hydroxide solution, concentration 4 mol/l.

Step 1	Balanced equation	$HCl_{(aq)}$	$+$	$NaOH_{(aq)}$	$\rightarrow$
				$NaCl_{(aq)}$	$+$ $H_2O_{(l)}$

Step 2	Relative number of moles	1 mol	1 mol

Step 3   Number of moles of $NaOH_{(aq)}$

$$1000 \text{ cm}^3 \quad \leftrightarrow \quad 4 \text{ mol}$$
$$20 \text{ cm}^3 \quad \leftrightarrow \quad 0.08 \text{ mol}$$

Step 4   Number of moles of $HCl_{(aq)}$ - from equation

0.08 mol

Step 5   Complete calculation

$$4 \text{ mol} \quad \leftrightarrow \quad 1000 \text{ cm}^3$$
$$0.08 \text{ mol} \quad \leftrightarrow \quad \textbf{40 cm}^3$$

❏   in a neutralisation reaction, neutralisation is complete
when all of the $H^+(aq)$ ions from the acid have reacted with
exactly the same number of $OH^-(aq)$ ions from the alkali

$$H^+(aq) \quad + \quad OH^-(aq) \quad \rightarrow \quad H_2O(l)$$

❏   the number of moles of $H^+(aq)$ which react will equal the
number of moles of $OH^-(aq)$ which react

❏   the relationship:

> volume x concentration (mol/l) x number of $H^+(aq)$
> in the formula
> =
> volume x concentration (mol/l) x number of $OH^-(aq)$
> in the formula

can be used to simplify calculations

Example 4

Calculate the volume of sodium hydroxide solution,
concentration 2 mol/l, which is required to neutralise
50 cm^3 of hydrochloric acid, concentration 1 mol/l .

Step 1	Write relationship	vol x conc x number of $H^+(aq)$ = vol x conc x number of $OH^-(aq)$
Step 2(a)	Number of $H^+(aq)$ in formula of acid	HCl(aq) 1
Step 2(a)	Number of $OH^-(aq)$ in formula of alkali	NaOH(aq) 1
Step 3	Put in variables	50 x 1 x 1 = V x 2 x 1
Step 4	Complete calculation	V = **25 cm^3**

Example 5

Calculate the volume of sulphuric acid, concentration 0.05 mol/l, which will neutralise 25 cm^3 of potassium hydroxide solution, concentration 0.1 mol/l.

Step 1	Write relationship	vol x conc x number of H$^+$(aq) = vol x conc x number of OH$^-$(aq)
Step 2(a)	Number of H$^+$(aq) in formula of acid	H_2SO_4 2
Step 2(a)	Number of OH$^-$(aq) in formula of alkali	KOH(aq) 1
Step 3	Put in variables	V x 0.05 x 2 = 25 x 0.1 x 1
Step 4	Complete calculation	V = **25 cm^3**

Gases

Collecting gases

❏ insoluble in water

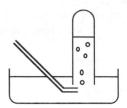

❏ soluble in water,
less dense than air

❏ soluble in water,
denser than air

Preparing gases

❏ e.g. hydrogen
(reactant - zinc),
carbon dioxide
(reactant - calcium carbonate)

acid

reactant

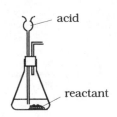

❏ e.g. ammonia

ammonium salt
+
base

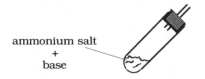

Tests

- **carbon dioxide gas** turns lime water milky

- **hydrogen gas** burns with a "pop"

- **oxygen gas** relights a glowing splint

- **acidic solutions** have a pH less than 7;
  turn Universal indicator solution
  pink / red

- **alkaline solutions** have a pH greater than 7;
  turn Universal indicator solution
  dark green / blue

- **alkenes** decolourise bromine solution

- **iron(II) ions** turn ferroxyl indicator solution blue
  (rusting)

- **glucose** turns Benedict's Reagent (Fehling's
  Reagent) orange / red

- **starch** turns iodine solution blue / black

- **fructose, maltose** also turn Benedict's Reagent
  (Fehling's reagent) orange / red

-

-

-

-

CREDIT

Chemical reactions

- **addition** : the reaction of an alkene in which a small molecule, e.g. bromine, is added across the carbon to carbon double bond to form a saturated product
- **burning** : reaction with oxygen
- **combustion** : another word for burning
- **corrosion** : the oxidation of a metal in the presence of oxygen and water
- **cracking** : the breaking down of long chain saturated hydrocarbons into a mixture of alkanes and alkenes
- **displacement** : the reaction in which a metal (or hydrogen) is formed from a solution of its ions by the addition of a more reactive metal
- **electrolysis** : the splitting up of an ionic compound using electricity; the ions in the compound must be free to move, i.e. in solution or a melt; a D.C. supply is used
- **electroplating** : the use of electrolysis to completely coat a metal with another metal which resists corrosion
- **fermentation** : the reaction which produces alcohol from glucose using zymase, an enzyme in yeast
- **fractional distillation** : the separation of a mixture of liquids by using the difference in their boiling points, e.g. fractional distillation of crude oil
- **galvanising** : the coating of a metal (usually iron) with zinc to protect it from corrosion
- **neutralisation** : the reaction of an acid with a neutraliser, e.g. alkali, to form a salt and water; the pH of the acid and alkali move towards 7
- **photosynthesis** : the production of glucose and oxygen by plants from carbon dioxide and water: the green colouring (chlorophyll) and sunlight are required
- **polymerisation** : the building up of large molecules (polymers) from small molecules (monomers)
- **precipitation** : the formation of an insoluble solid when certain solutions are mixed together
- **respiration** : the release of energy in living things caused by the reaction of glucose with oxygen; carbon dioxide and water are also produced
- **rusting** : the corrosion of iron

- **addition poymerisation** : the joining up of unsaturated molecules (monomers), e.g. alkenes, by the opening of the carbon to carbon double bond to form a large molecule (addition polymer)
- **condensation polymerisation** : the joining up of small molecules (monomers) to form a large molecule (condensation polymer) with the loss of water
- **hydrolysis** : the reaction in which a large molecule is broken down by the addition of water
- **oxidation** : the loss of electrons from a substance in a chemical reaction
- **redox** : the reaction which involves both oxidation and reduction
- **reduction** : the gain of electrons by a substance in a chemical reaction

CREDIT